INTRODUCTION TO NUCLEAR SCIENCE

ARGONNE NATIONAL LABORATORY

Operated by the University of Chicago
for the United States Atomic Energy Commission

CONTRIBUTORS

Max D. Adams
Jerome E. Baird
William C. Bentley
Birute O. Biskis
Bernhard Blumenthal
Robert F. Buchanan
Donald Cohen
John G. Cunninghame
Nicola D'Angelo
Charles F. Ehret
Asher J. Finkel
Miriam P. Finkel
Kevin F. Flynn
Robert J. Friddle
Leonard S. Goodman
Sheffield Gordon
Douglas Grahn
Elsie Gulyas
David C. Hess
Charles M. Huddleston
Bernard N. Jaroslow
Manuel A. Kanter
Leonard I. Katzin
Walter E. Kisieleski
Peter D. Klein
Herbert E. Kubitschek
Jerome L. Lerner
Harold A. May

Luise S. Meyer
William A. Mulac
William F. Murphy
Michael V. Nevitt
Donald F. Peppard
Earl W. Phelan
Edward L. Powers
Richard S. Preston
Frederick G. Prohammer
Anthony R. Sallese
John Skok
Douglas E. Smith
Bernard I. Spinrad
Henry E. Stanton
Andrew F. Stehney
Robert L. Straube
George Svihla
Robert W. Swick
Lyman J. Templin
Lee C. Teng
George E. Thomas, Jr.
John F. Thomson
Francis E. Throw
Howard H. Vogel
Ronald Watanabe
James L. Weeks
Walter D. Wilkinson
Philip H. Yuster

INTRODUCTION TO
NUCLEAR SCIENCE

by

ALVIN GLASSNER
Argonne National Laboratory

D. VAN NOSTRAND COMPANY, INC.
PRINCETON, NEW JERSEY

TORONTO   LONDON

NEW YORK

D. VAN NOSTRAND COMPANY, INC.
120 Alexander St., Princeton, New Jersey (*Principal office*)
24 West 40 Street, New York 18, New York

D. VAN NOSTRAND COMPANY, LTD.
358, Kensington High Street, London, W.14, England

D. VAN NOSTRAND COMPANY (Canada), LTD.
25 Hollinger Road, Toronto 16, Canada

PREFACE

In December, 1956, a committee of the Argonne National Laboratory Branch of the Scientific Research Society of America (RESA) proposed that there be given, during the summer of 1957, a short, intensive course for high school science teachers on the fundamentals of science related to activities at Argonne. The proposals of the committee were a consequence of editorial appeal in the *American Scientist* for activity on the part of Sigma Xi and RESA groups directed toward the improvement of science education in the secondary schools.

The course was designed to narrow the gap between the training of the average high school teacher and the current state of scientific knowledge. In view of the unique position of the Laboratory and its facilities, coupled with a staff of diversified talents, the decision was made to limit the sessions to the field of the nuclear sciences and to parts of the natural sciences touching on that field. The intention was to survey the field, highlighting recent developments, rather than to study intensively any particular segment. This was of particular importance, since the high school teachers were expected to have various backgrounds and to be responsible for single subjects varying from biology to physics.

It was also desired to emphasize the experimental and laboratory aspects of science. The hope was that, upon returning to their schools, teachers would be able to duplicate and illustrate in their classrooms some fundamental phenomena and principles. Demonstrations and experiments were therefore to be stripped, as far as possible, of accessories and expensive instrumentation.

The course was to be made as short as possible, since summer has been a period in which the teacher either takes another job to make up financial deficiencies or attends summer classes to obtain credits which meet educational requirements for an increase in salary. Accordingly, the course was established with a lecture and a "laboratory" each half-day for thirteen class days. This included a half-day for registration and orientation at the beginning and a terminal half-day for comments, criticisms, résumés, and "commencement."

Lectures were usually given by experts in the field, who took pains to keep them at an appropriate nontechnical level. Mathematics was employed only to the extent that the diversified backgrounds of the teachers would permit. The laboratory experiments were chosen and developed to demonstrate the fundamental principles stressed in the course. Tours of the Laboratory facilities were arranged in conjunction with the appropriate lectures. A large amount of supplementary printed reference material from the Atomic Energy Commission, Laboratory, and commercial sources was given to the teachers. In addition, they

v

took home some materials, such as irradiated sunflower seeds, samples of a uranium mineral, sections of a teacher-made fuel element.

With the consent and approval of the Laboratory Director, Dr. Norman Hilberry, and with the enthusiastic support and guidance of the Director of Technical Information, Dr. Hoylande D. Young, the course was given twice in the summer of 1957 under the directorship of Dr. Leonard I. Katzin, three times during the summer of 1958 and again in the summer of 1959, under the directorship of the author.

The Argonne "teachers" devoted their talents and time voluntarily to this undertaking. Without them this book would not have been written. Their lectures have been "plagiarized" and their experiments have been reprinted. Theirs should really be the credit.

A. G.

CONTENTS

SUMMARY OF CURRICULUM

UNIT	TOPIC	NUMBER OF LECTURES	LABORATORY
I	Atomic Structure and Energetics	2	(1) Assembly of e/m Apparatus (2) Tour of Various Mass Spectrometers at Argonne
II	Radioactivity and Radiations	3	(1) Construction of Cloud Chamber (2) Assembly of Electroscope (3) Demonstration of Absorption and Inverse-Square Law of Radiations
III	Nuclear Reactions, Nuclear Structure, and Nucleons	2	(1) Tour of the Cyclotron, Van de Graaff, and Linear Accelerator (2) Tracing Radioactive Decay
IV	Reactors	2	(1) Tour of CP-5 and EBWR (2) Tour of Argonaut
V	Radiation Effects in Solids and Liquids	2	(1) Tour of Radiation Laboratories in Chemistry Division (2) Actinometer

CHAPTER I

THE NUCLEAR ATOM

1.1. THE ATOM

Today people accept as a fact that all ordinary matter consists of atoms. No one has ever seen an atom; its existence is purely inferential. Yet we are as convinced of the physical reality of the atom as we are of our own existence. If there is one basic idea behind all of modern science, it is that of the atom.

The word "atom" is derived from the Greek language and means something that is not divisible. The concept can be traced at least to the fifth century B.C. and is ascribed to Leucippus and Democritus, two Greek philosophers who believed that all material things were composed ultimately of exceedingly small, individual units.

If a piece of chalk is ground, the result is merely a fine chalk dust. If this dust is rubbed against a blackboard, a white mark will remain. Any chemical analysis reveals that the dust has the same composition and chemical properties as the larger piece. If the chalk is ground so as to produce smaller and yet smaller particles, will it always remain chalk? Insofar as any experiment has been carried out, the answer is yes. There seems to be no limit, experimentally, to the smallness of the particle obtained by grinding. Why, then, should a Democritus or an Empedocles believe that there is some final piece of chalk, howsoever small, which cannot be made smaller?

The answer to this question lies in the nature of the philosophy which appealed to the Greek intellect. The Greeks, as we do today, believed that natural phenomena were the results of hidden occurrences. In order to explain such phenomena, then, it was necessary to determine the nature of these hidden occurrences. Superimposed on this was a belief in the existence of something permanent in Nature. Behind all the multitudes of changes there existed something immutable and never-changing. It was the search for this hidden permanence, this unaltered "being," that led to the concept of the atom. The atoms were considered to be impenetrable, unchangeable, and eternal (a description which would have probably been acceptable to scientists a scant seventy-five years ago). The atoms of a given kind differed from atoms of another kind in shape and in size, but what the shapes and the sizes might be were unknown.

Natural phenomena were to be explained in terms of the motions of atoms through empty space. It was these motions that gave rise to sensations of warmth, light, color, smell, and so on. The atom served as the building block of

1

the world; there was no further mystery. Material objects were simple conglomerations of large numbers of these particles (how many?) in definite spatial patterns determined by the shapes of the atoms. It was the changes in relative positions among the atoms that produced and explained all natural changes. (Do we perceive here the influence of the Greek preoccupation with form and geometry, a concern with size, shape, and position?) The atom was the "true" reality.

The atomic theory of the Greeks lived awhile and then died, perhaps because neither theoretical nor experimental science was yet prepared to "prove" the existence of atoms or was it able to follow through the conclusions of an atomic theory with mathematical thoroughness or testable precision. Atomism was a purely qualitative, almost indefinite concept, vying with other qualitative theories to explain and understand nature. The acceptance of one or another of these theories was essentially dependent upon the individual's beliefs and satisfaction of his aesthetic sensibilities. There were no experimental data on which to base a choice. Perhaps Democritus simply refused to believe that there could be no limit to a process of continuous division of matter. His atomic theory satisfied his philosophic preconceptions concerning a fundamental simplicity of Nature.

The death of Greek atomism may be surprising because the basic idea is closely akin to the atomic theory of today, which forms the foundation of every branch of science. But, like Anaximander's premature ideas of evolution, the Greek theory was sterile. The usefulness of an atomic theory had to wait until there was a background of fertile soil upon which it could grow and secure nourishment. It had to be delayed for the beginnings of a science of chemistry, for the growth of experimental techniques, and for the development of suitable mathematical procedures.

The revival of the atom as a scientific concept came early in the nineteenth century as a result of efforts to explain some fundamental chemical phenomena. Credit for originating the modern atomic theory is usually given to the English schoolteacher John Dalton. By showing how the weights of different atoms relative to one another could be determined, he made the theory quantitative instead of philosophically speculative.

Dalton proposed the idea that the few elements which compose all substances are made of atoms and that all the atoms of a given element are alike. He further suggested that the atoms of different elements differ in weight. When atoms combined with other atoms to form molecules ("compound atoms"), each kind of molecule consisted of a definite integral number of atoms of each constituent element. Dalton assumed that the atoms remained essentially unchanged in forming a molecule, so that the weight of the molecule was simply the sum of the weights of the constituent atoms. The mass of water formed from hydrogen and oxygen was simply equal to the combined masses of these chemical elements that entered into chemical reaction. The conservation of mass was a basic concept inherent in Dalton's theory. In this way he could explain the chemical laws of definite and of multiple proportions.

It was this successful use of an atomic theory to elucidate in a quantitative fashion a set of experimentally observed facts that differentiated Dalton's proposals from the speculations of Democritus. Dalton's idea of *constancy of weight* eliminated the considerations of undetectable differences in size and shape as the basic distinction among the various types of atoms. Sizes and shapes of invisible particles could not be determined; nor could such qualities be found by considering conglomerations of such particles. But the weight of any conglomeration would be simply the sum of the weights of the individual atoms constituting that conglomeration. If one knew the number of atoms in a conglomeration of a given kind, it would be a simple matter to determine the weight of the individual atom. Fortunately, the state of chemical science in Dalton's time did not require the knowledge of such an absolute weight; it was merely necessary to compare the relative weights of the different atoms, say, with the weight of an atom of the lightest element, hydrogen, chosen as unity, or with the oxygen atom chosen as standard. The relative weights of the atoms could be determined as proportional to the experimentally measured combining weights of the elements. (This was, of course, an error, but was corrected through the work of Avogadro, Gay-Lussac, and Cannizzaro.)

It is possible that the concept of atoms arose in Dalton's mind in the form of Newton's hard, massive particles. Dalton extended the concept by implying that, in addition to the mechanical forces they were supposed to exert, the atoms somehow or other possessed "chemical forces." Further, Newton's "particle" was a point mass, a concept convenient in mathematical discussions. The atom of Dalton, however, was the ultimate physical unit of matter; division of such an atom into something smaller would be unimaginable, because it would be meaningless. What would be formed? To divide a molecule of, say, water would conceivably give back hydrogen and oxygen atoms, but what would result if a hydrogen atom were divided? It could not be a smaller hydrogen atom, because by definition the atom was the smallest unit of hydrogen which could take part in chemical reactions. The scientific world was not yet ready to conceive that atoms had internal structures, that the atoms of the chemical elements were themselves composed of even more fundamental particles. Where was there any evidence for such a possibility? On the other hand, does a simple difference in weight between a hydrogen atom and an oxygen atom account for the differences in their properties? What factors determine this difference in weight? Why do these atoms show great differences in their abilities to combine chemically? What connection is there between the atoms and the observation that an electric current can cause the occurrence of chemical reactions?

1.2. THE ELECTRON

Matter is normally electrically neutral. Yet even the ancient Greeks knew that some forms of matter — amber, glass, etc. — become electrified when rubbed with cloth or fur, for example. This kind of electrification was called static or frictional electricity. For a long time this was considered to be different from flowing electricity, discovered by Galvani and Volta in the eighteenth century. In the early years of the nineteenth century the electric current that flows in a wire was thought to be a continuous fluid in motion. It was not until Faraday established the laws of electrolysis that the corpuscular nature of electricity was suspected. This idea received added support when cathode rays, produced by causing an electric current to pass through a highly rarefied gas under high potential, were discovered. Since then numerous experiments have established the corpuscular nature of electricity, although developments in the past thirty years indicate that the concept of corpuscles is far from being as clear-cut as was formerly believed.

When an electric discharge is passed through a gas at low pressure, the tube in the vicinity of the cathode (the electrode attached to the negative side of the source of potential) emits a greenish glow. It was deduced that the glow was caused by "rays" originating at the cathode. Such rays were consequently called cathode rays. They were found to be deflected by magnetic fields and, since they were able to cast a shadow of an obstacle placed in their path, to travel in straight lines. They possessed sufficient momentum to cause a small paddle wheel to rotate.

William Crookes concluded from his studies that the cathode rays actually consisted of a stream of negatively charged particles moving with very high speeds. Some objection to this was made by other scientists: if the rays were actually a stream of charged particles, they should be deflected by an electric field, which they had not yet been able to demonstrate.

In 1897, however, the English physicist J. J. Thomson definitely proved that the rays were made of negative particles emitted from the cathode. Further, he succeeded in deflecting the path of cathode rays by means of an electrical field. Previous failures had been due to ionization of the gas still present in the discharge tube, which offset the effect of the applied electric field. Thomson overcame this by the simple expedient of further reducing the pressure.

If a stream of charged particles moving initially in a straight line is passed through a magnetic field applied perpendicularly to the direction of motion, the particles will follow a circular path. If q denotes the magnitude of the charge carried by the particle and v its speed, then Hqv will be the magnetic force acting on the particle by a magnetic field of strength H. The magnetic force Hqv provides the centripetal force, mv^2/r, of the particle of mass m moving along the circular path of radius r, i.e.,

$$Hqv = mv^2/r, \qquad\qquad (\text{I.2-1})$$

so

$$q/m = v/Hr \qquad\qquad (\text{I.2-2})$$

is the ratio of the charge to the mass (that is, the specific charge) of the moving charged particles.

Now by definition Eq is the force acting on a charged particle in an electric field of strength E. If, in a new experiment, the electric and magnetic fields can be so arranged that their effects on a moving charged particle exactly compensate each other, so that the particle is not deflected from its path, then the forces produced are equal:

$$Hqv = Eq. \tag{I.2-3}$$

Hence

$$v = E/H. \tag{I.2-4}$$

It thus becomes possible to measure the speed of motion of an electrically charged particle by measuring the strengths of compensating electric and magnetic fields. Further, introduction of equation (I.2-4) into equation (I.2-2) gives

$$q/m = E/H^2r, \tag{I.2-5}$$

allowing the specific charge to be determined from the field strengths and the radius of the path in the magnetic field alone, all of which can be measured.

Thomson found that the cathode-ray particles could move with speeds up to the enormous value of 3×10^9 cm/sec (about one-tenth of the speed of light). The specific charge was about -2×10^{17} esu/gm.[1] Further, Thomson's results were the same for different cathode materials (aluminum, iron, and platinum) and for different gases (air, hydrogen, and carbon dioxide) present in the discharge tube. Clearly the constancy of the specific charge indicated that the same kind of particle was obtained as well from one kind of matter as from another: the particles seemed to be a universal constituent of all matter. The name *electron*, suggested by Stoney in 1891 and originally intended to describe the magnitude of the electronic charge, is the term commonly used for these particles.

It is comparatively easy to measure the charge of an electron, the absolute magnitude of which is denoted by e. One of the most elegant ways of measuring e was devised by Millikan in his famous oil-drop experiment. The charge of the electron turns out to be extremely small: -4.80×10^{-10} esu ($= -1.6 \times 10^{-19}$ coulomb). A current of 1 milliampere represents the passage of about 6×10^{15} electrons/sec. Together with the value of e/m for the electron this permits a calculation of the mass of the electron: 9×10^{-28} gm. On the usual chemical atomic weight scale, with atmospheric oxygen assigned a value of 16.000, the weight of an electron is 0.000548.

[1]More accurate results indicate a specific charge of about -5.3×10^{17} esu/gm. This value is about 1850 times greater than for a hydrogen ion in solution. Thomson's result was low because the apparent mass of an electron increases, in accordance with the theory of relativity, with the speed with which it is moving, an effect that is apparent only when the speed is an appreciable fraction of the velocity of light.

Electrons have been found to be set free from matter in a variety of ways: by flames and hot wires (the thermionic effect), illumination with ultraviolet light or X rays (the photoelectric effect), and so on. No electric charge smaller than that of the electron has ever been observed, and every measured charge appears to be some integral multiple of the absolute value of the electronic charge. It is apparent that an electric charge, like an atom, cannot be subdivided indefinitely. The electrons must be fundamental constituents of all atoms. Today we still do not know just exactly what electrons are or whether they have some kind of internal structure.

I.3. THE MASS SPECTROGRAPH AND ISOTOPES

After the electron was discovered, it was natural, considering the neutrality of ordinary matter, to search for a particle carrying a corresponding positive charge. In 1886 the German physicist E. Goldstein had used a perforated metal disc as the

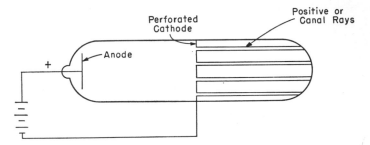

FIG. I.3-1. *Schematic representation of the apparatus for obtaining positive rays.*

cathode of a gaseous-discharge tube at high vacuum (see Fig. I.3-1). He observed luminous rays (called *canal rays*) emerging in straight lines from the holes of the cathode on the sides opposite to the anode. In the late 1890's it was shown that these rays were associated with positive charges and that they could be deflected by electric and magnetic fields. J. J. Thomson in 1907 proposed the more appropriate name of *positive rays.*

In principle, the method used to find the mass of an electron is equally applicable to the measurement of the mass of *any* charged body, and thus of the positive rays. In practice, the large ratio of mass to charge requires much modification of the apparatus used in the case of electrons. Several types of *mass spectrographs* or *mass spectrometers* (the choice of name depending on the particular method of detection employed), instruments to measure the masses of ions, have been developed to yield results with very high precision.

The essential features of the simplest mass spectrometers differ from the apparatus used to measure the ratio of charge to mass in the case of the electron in that (a) the larger masses of ions require the use of much larger accelerating voltages and of much more intense fields, and (*b*) the sources of ions are somewhat more complicated than the source of electrons. In addition, different types of detection equipment are usually employed.

Fig. I.3-2 is a schematic diagram of such an instrument. The ions are formed in the ion source and are accelerated through a large difference of potential, V_{acc}, between collimating slits A and B. They are then deflected in the field of the analyzing magnet and detected after passing through slit C.

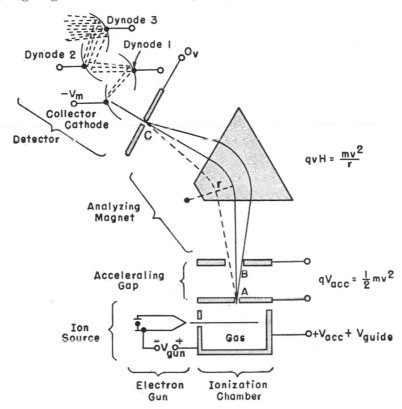

FIG. I.3-2. *Schematic representation of a mass spectrometer.*

Different types of ion sources are used for different purposes. There are, however, several standard types. (1) One such source consists of a specially treated surface which emits a few positive ions among the much more numerous neutral atoms evaporated when the surface is heated. In spite of the limited numbers of ions produced, this source has the advantage that the ions have very small initial energies, so that after acceleration all have very nearly the same speed. (2) A much larger selection of ions can be produced in electric arcs or, for the most refractory elements, in an electric spark between electrodes made of (or loaded with) the material to be studied. The ions are produced with a quite appreciable spread of energies. (3) The type of ion source depicted in Fig. I.3-2 is widely used when the material to be ionized is a gas. In the electron gun, the electrons "boiled" from the hot filament are accelerated in an electric field. Some of these pass through a small hole in the side of the ionization chamber to form a narrow beam through the contained gas. Ionization of the gas, which is supplied continuously through a slow leak from a tank or bulb, occurs as a result of the electron bombardment.

The positive ions emerging through the source slit A are accelerated by the difference in potential V_{acc} and acquire a kinetic energy given by the equation

$$qV_{acc} = \tfrac{1}{2}mv^2, \tag{I.3-1}$$

where m is the mass of the positively charged particle, q its charge, and v its speed. In the actual instrument, some additional slits, placed in the accelerating gap at intermediate voltages, are used to focus the beam more sharply.

Between slits B and C the beam is in a region at ground potential. In this region the beam passes through the gap between the poles of a sizable analyzing magnet, where the uniform field produces a deflection of the beam. In common practice the beam is deflected through an angle of 60°. Here, as in the case with electrons,

$$mv/q = Hr, \tag{I.3-2}$$

that is, all the ions with the same momentum mv and the same charge q will be deflected in the magnetic field of strength H through an arc of the same radius r. By a combination of equations (I.3-1) and (I.3-2), there is obtained

$$q/m = 2V_{acc}/H^2r^2. \tag{I.3-3}$$

The analyzing magnet also serves to focus the beam, but the solid line in Fig. I.3-2 represents the center of the beam of ions. Ions following the dotted path on the "outside" of the turn have a longer arc of the same radius in the magnetic field; hence, they are bent back to enter slit C. Ions following the dashed path on the "inside" of the turn have a smaller arc to travel; they are deflected less than those following the solid line, so that they also enter slit C. This focusing on slit C is achieved only for proper adjustment of H and V_{acc}.

The first mass spectrometers, built by Thomson in 1907 and by Aston in 1919, detected the ions by the blackening produced where they struck a photographic plate at the position of slit C. Later machines used a collector cup to catch the ion beam and measured the current by measuring the rate at which a small capacitor, connected to an electrometer, was charged. The "electron multiplier" illustrated in Fig. I.3-2 is a recent innovation. It makes use of the phenomenon of *secondary emission*, whereby an energetic particle striking a surface causes the release of electrons. The average number of electrons ejected per incident particle depends on the energy of the latter and may be as high as 4, 5, or more for a sensitive surface.

In the electron multiplier shown, the ions strike the collector cathode and secondary electrons are produced. Under the influence of an appropriate voltage, these secondary electrons are accelerated to the first dynode where each ejects secondary electrons; these, in turn, are accelerated to the second dynode, etc. If there are N secondary electrons ejected per incident particle and there are s stages of multiplication, then N^s electrons reach the anode for each ion striking the collector cathode. The electron multiplication factor N is commonly between 2 and 3; also, s may be from 8 to 16. Thus, the overall multiplication factor may be from $2^8 = 256$ to $3^{16} \sim 4 \times 10^7$. Detectors which have large multiplication factors may count individual ions as they arrive, so that very weak sources and very small samples may be used. Mass spectrometers have been designed for very precise work. Such machines may achieve an accuracy as good as 1 part in 10^8 and may detect as little as 10^{-17} gm of some elements.

The values of the ratios of charge to mass for positive-ray particles were found to be very much smaller than the corresponding value for an electron. In general, the masses of the positively charged particles were found to be some thousands of times greater than that of the electron and corresponded to the masses of the gas molecules present in the discharge tube. The specific charges were very nearly the same as obtained by chemists from electrolysis experiments. The positively charged particles were actually atomic or molecular ions, formed by stripping electrons from the atoms or molecules of the gas in the process called ionization.

The lightest particle observed in the positive rays had the same mass as the hydrogen atom and carried one (unit) positive charge, equal in magnitude but of opposite sign to the charge carried by an electron. In other words, it was the singly charged hydrogen ion H^+, presumably formed by the removal of an electron from a hydrogen atom.

In the course of experiments with neon (atomic weight 20.2) in 1913, J. J. Thomson always found the presence of particles of masses 20 and 22 on the atomic weight scale. After being satisfied that the particle of mass 22 was not an impurity, Thomson could only conclude that neon was a mixture of gases, one having an atomic weight of about 20 and the other having an atomic weight of about 22. Aston, who was then an assistant to Thomson, actually effected a partial separation of these gases by a diffusion method.

The term *isotope* is used (as proposed by Fajans and Soddy to indicate that they occupy the same place in the periodic series of elements) for atomic species of the same element which have different masses but the same chemical properties. (Actually, isotopes were discovered in connection with the phenomenon of radioactivity, considered in § I.4.) Thomson showed that neon consisted of two isotopes (a third isotope of mass about 21 is now known). Most of the chemical elements as found in nature are composed of mixtures of isotopes. The results of investigations with mass spectrographs indicate that the elements possess, on the average, more than three stable isotopes each. Of course some, such as beryllium, have only one, whereas, for example, tin has as many as ten. Isotopy seems to be the rule, rather than the exception, among all the elements.

The stable isotopes of a given element generally occur together in nature in constant proportions. This explains why atomic weight determinations on samples of a given element from widely different sources generally agree within experimental errors. It would appear that in the evolution of the elements the various isotopes were produced in the same proportions and these have remained constant. (This is not true in the case of radioactive isotopes, of course.)

Determinations of atomic weights by chemical methods give the average weight of a large number of atoms of a given element. Modern mass spectrographs measure the masses of the individual isotopes, the *isotopic weights*, and are capable of an accuracy much greater than that of any chemical method. Very few elements have exactly integral atomic weights as measured chemically. In fact these fractional atomic weights, such as of chlorine (35.46), were long a puzzle. But measurements of isotopic masses by the use of mass spectrographs have given values which are very nearly whole numbers. Some isotopic weights are slightly less than integers, and others are somewhat greater. With the exception of the heavy radioactive elements, the maximum deviation is about 0.06 atomic mass unit (amu), most of the differences being considerably smaller. The integer nearest the isotopic weight, which is commonly used to identify the isotope, was called the *mass number* by Aston.

The scale of atomic weights used in chemistry is based on the arbitrary selection of an atomic weight of 16.000 for natural oxygen. All other atomic weights of the elements are obtained from measurements of their combining weights, using natural oxygen as the standard. Actually, natural oxygen is a mixture of three isotopes, having mass numbers of 16, 17, and 18. The isotope with mass number 16 is by far the most abundant. Physicists have chosen to use this most abundant isotope as a standard of reference, assigning it an isotopic mass of exactly 16. For atmospheric oxygen, the following data are available:

MASS OF ISOTOPE (PHYSICAL SCALE)	PER CENT ABUNDANCE
16.000000	99.758
17.004534	0.0373
18.004855	0.2039

The average mass of this mixture as computed from the relative abundances is 16.004452. Since this quantity is taken as exactly 16.000 on the chemical scale, we find that

$$\text{Mass on chemical scale} = \frac{\text{mass on physical scale}}{1.000278}. \qquad (I.3\text{-}4)$$

The symbol used to denote a nuclear species is the chemical symbol of the element with the atomic number Z as a left subscript and the mass number as a right superscript. Thus $_2\text{He}^4$ denotes the nucleus of helium with a mass number of 4, and $_{92}\text{U}^{235}$ denotes that of a uranium nucleus of mass number 235. The atomic number Z is often omitted because it is uniquely determined by the chemical symbol. The two examples may then be written as He^4 and U^{235}.

Table I.3-1 gives the isotopic weights of some of the isotopes of the lighter elements.

TABLE I.3-1

ATOMIC WEIGHTS OF SOME LIGHT ISOTOPES

Element	Isotopic Weight (physical scale)
Hydrogen	1.008145
	2.014740
Helium	4.003873
Lithium	6.017034
	7.018232
Beryllium	8.007849
	9.015046
Boron	10.016119
	11.012705
Carbon	12.003803
	13.007478
Nitrogen	14.007520
	15.004862
Oxygen	16.000000
	17.004534
	18.004855
Fluorine	19.004448

I.4. RADIOACTIVITY

Many substances when exposed to ultraviolet light or X rays become copious emitters of visible light. In some of these materials the emission of visible light persists long after the exposure to radiation, as in the case of the luminous dial of a watch. In many other substances the glowing lasts only a fraction of a second after the excitation has ceased. The former phenomenon is called phosphorescence and the latter is termed fluorescence.

While studying the phosphorescence of various materials and the possible connection with the newly discovered X rays of Roentgen, Henri Becquerel in 1896 was led to the discovery of radioactivity. He noticed that several salts of uranium emitted an invisible radiation capable of traversing thin layers of opaque materials and affecting a photographic plate. After careful investigation Becquerel concluded that the radiation was not attributable to a phosphorescence, that is, it was not dependent upon any primary exciting radiation. He also observed that the air near the uranium salts became electrically conducting and thus capable of discharging an electroscope.

Mme. Curie, in extensive studies of this new phenomenon, to which she gave the appropriate name of radioactivity, found that thorium possessed similar properties. She found that the activity was proportional solely to the amounts of uranium and thorium present, regardless of their states of chemical combination. Thus Mme. Curie decided that this radioactivity must be an atomic phenomenon. In further investigations, the Curies were led to the discovery of polonium and radium. At present more than forty naturally radioactive species of high atomic weight are known. The fact that all these radioactive elements are grouped at the end of the periodic table must in some way be connected with an apparently increasing complexity of the atom with increasing mass.

Becquerel, the Curies, and others found that radioactivity was not affected by change of temperature nor by any other available physical or chemical means. It was entirely spontaneous. This represented a different behavior from that exhibited by the rates of the usual chemical changes. It tended to confirm the hypothesis that this phenomenon must be one occurring within the atom, that is, must be some kind of subatomic change.

In 1899 it was observed that the radiations from radioactive materials could be deflected in a magnetic field in the same direction as are cathode rays. It there-fore appeared that at least part of the radiations consisted of negatively charged particles. At about the same time, Rutherford in England, studying the extent to which passage through thin sheets of aluminum reduced the ionizing power of the radiations, concluded that the radiations from uranium were of at least two different types. One type, called *alpha* (*α*) *rays* by Rutherford, were unable to penetrate more than about 0.002 cm of aluminum. The second kind, *beta* (*β*) *rays*, required a much thicker sheet for complete absorption. The penetrating power of the beta rays was found to be approximately one hundred times that of the alpha rays.

A third type of radiation, now called *gamma* (*γ*) *radiation*, was discovered by P. Villard in 1900. Gamma rays were not deflected by a magnetic field, but they possessed considerable penetrating power and could markedly affect photo-graphic plates. It was not until 1914 that gamma rays were shown to have a wave nature similar to that of X rays, but of very high frequency, and thus to be a form of electromagnetic radiation.

In 1900 the Curies showed that beta rays were associated with a negative electrical charge. It was later established, with complete certainty, that beta rays did consist of electrons moving at very high speeds. A beta particle is thus identical with an electron.

Deflections of alpha rays in electric and magnetic fields indicated that these were associated with positively charged particles. More refined experiments led to the conclusion that an alpha particle was a doubly ionized helium atom, He^{++}. By permitting alpha rays to pass through a very thin glass wall into an evacuated glass vessel, sufficient gas was collected to allow its detection as helium by means of the spectroscope.

I.5. THE NUCLEAR ATOM

Gone now was the simple picture of an atom as a billiard ball, unalterable and eternal. In its place was a sort of electrically neutral structure which contained some easily detachable electrons. Where did the radiations arise? What kind of structure did an atom have? J. J. Thomson proposed a model in which the atom was assumed to consist of a number of electrons moving in a uniform, spherically shaped charge cloud of positive electricity. But such a model turned out to be incapable of explaining some simple observed facts.

At first it was believed that alpha particles traveled in straight, undeviating lines when allowed to pass through matter. More careful observation showed that a portion of an alpha beam was in general deviated through small angles, depending upon the kind and the thickness of the material. The heavier the element and the less the velocity of the alpha particle, the greater was the deviation. Occasionally a few particles (about 1 in 8000) were found to be deflected as much as 90° or more.

Initially the interpretation had been made that these large deflections must be due to multiple encounters between the alpha particle and the atoms of the transmitting material, for it was thought, in accordance with the Thomson model, that whatever electric field existed within the atom could not be of sufficient intensity to deflect seriously such a heavy body as an alpha particle in a single encounter. In 1911 Rutherford proposed that, assuming electrostatic forces of repulsion were responsible, these large deflections must be due to a single encounter, as the probability of one particle already largely deflected having a second encounter of the same sort was very small. For this to be possible, it was necessary to suppose that there was an intense electric field near an atom. He postulated that the total positive charge of the atom was concentrated in a small center or *nucleus*, not distributed throughout the atom as Thomson had supposed, but presumably situated at the center of the atom, and that the equal negative charge in the form of electrons was distributed over the much larger domain of the remainder of the atom. An alpha particle should be able to penetrate very close to the nucleus before the large repulsive force would deflect the particle through a large angle. At the same time, an alpha particle near the nucleus is relatively far from the negative charges (all charges being assumed to act as point charges), so that any attractive force exerted on the alpha particle by the electrons can be neglected. Only the central positive charge need be considered for any deflection greater than about 1°. The force between this positively charged nucleus and the positive alpha particle was considered to be a simple repulsion in accordance with Coulomb's law: the force of repulsion between two similar charges is proportional to the product of the charges divided by the square of the distance between them. The path of an alpha particle, assuming the mass of the scattering nucleus to be sufficiently heavy to remain at rest, would then be one branch of a hyperbola with the nucleus as the external focus (see Fig. I.5-1). The initial path of the particle is AO, one of the asymptotes of the hyperbola. On approaching the nucleus, the alpha particle is deflected through the angle φ and approaches the asymptote OA′.

When the alpha particle is at a great distance from the nucleus, its potential

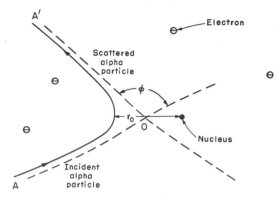

FIG. I.5-1. *The scattering of an alpha particle by a nucleus.*

energy, which is inversely proportional to this distance, is practically zero. If v_α is its velocity at this large (infinite) separation, its total energy is equal to its initial kinetic energy, $\frac{1}{2}m_\alpha v_\alpha^2$, where m_α is its mass. This energy must also be equal to the total energy of the alpha particle when it is at the distance of closest approach (the vertex of the hyperbola). If the velocity at this point is $v_{\alpha,0}$, then by the law of conservation of energy

$$\tfrac{1}{2}m_\alpha v_\alpha^2 = \tfrac{1}{2}m_\alpha v_{\alpha,0}^2 + (2eQ_n/r_0), \tag{I.5-1}$$

where $2e$ is the charge of the alpha particle and Q_n that of the nucleus. The second term on the right-hand side of Equation I.5-1 represents the electrostatic potential energy of the alpha particle at the vertex of its orbit in the field of the nucleus.

The distance of nearest approach will be a minimum r_0 for an alpha particle striking a nucleus directly, and in this case of a "head-on collision" the alpha particle will be scattered through 180°, that is, back along its original path. At the turning point, $v_{\alpha,0} = 0$. Hence from Equation I.5-1 there is obtained

$$\tfrac{1}{2}m_\alpha v_\alpha^2 = 2eQ_n/r_0. \tag{I.5-2}$$

Upon algebraic transformation there is obtained

$$r_0 = 4eQ_n/m_\alpha v_\alpha^2. \tag{I.5-3}$$

Experimental measurements indicated that the distance of closest approach of fast alpha particles was of the order of 10^{-12} cm. This figure, then, represents an upper limit to the diameter of a nucleus. From X-ray studies of crystal structure and from the kinetic theory of gases the diameters of atoms have been established as being of the order of 10^{-8} cm. It is seen that the diameter of the nucleus must be only a very small fraction of the atomic diameter. The volume of the nucleus is calculated to be about 10^{-36} cc, whereas the effective volume of an atom is approximately 10^{-24} cc. Because of the small size of the nucleus, only a minor proportion of the impinging alpha particles would come close enough to experience a strong repulsion.

Using the theory of probability, Rutherford was able to derive an expression for the number of alpha particles scattered through an angle φ to unit area of a detector placed at a distance R from a thin foil containing n atoms per unit volume:

$$Y = Int(Q_n e/m_\alpha v_\alpha{}^2)(1/R^2)\csc^4\tfrac{1}{2}\varphi, \qquad (\text{I.5-4})$$

where I is the total number of alpha particles incident on the foil of thickness t. A very thorough test of this equation by Geiger and Marsden in 1913 gave results in good agreement with Rutherford's predictions about the dependence of the scattering on the angle of deflection, on the thickness of foil, and on the velocity (or energy) of the alpha particle. This was interpreted as establishing the correctness of the concept of the nuclear atom. Although not sufficiently precise to permit an accurate determination, the data obtained led to an indication that the number of unit (electronic) positive charges on the nucleus, symbolized by Z, was approximately one-half the atomic mass. Because of the electrical neutrality of the atom as a whole, the positive charge on the nucleus must be balanced by an equal number Z of negative charges in the form of electrons. It followed, therefore, that the number of electrons must be roughly equal to one-half of the atomic mass and hence would not greatly exceed 100, even for the heaviest elements. These experiments confirmed data of Barkla, who also found, on the basis of the scattering of X rays by several light elements, that the number of electrons in an atom was approximately equal to one-half the atomic weight. Further, since the mass of an electron is approximately $\frac{1}{2000}$ that of a hydrogen atom, about 100 electrons would represent no more than about a mass of 0.05 on the ordinary scale of atomic weights. Essentially, then, almost all of the mass of an atom, as well as all of its positive charge Ze, must be concentrated in the nucleus.

In 1913 the Dutch physicist Van den Brock suggested that the number of positive charges on the nucleus of any given atom is equal to the ordinal number (now called the *atomic number*, as proposed by Moseley) of the particular element in the periodic system. Thus the atomic number Z for hydrogen would be 1, for helium 2, for lithium 3 .... More precise scattering experiments with several elements by Chadwick in 1920 did indeed lead to a positive charge on the nucleus in excellent agreement with the respective atomic number. As a result of these and other observations it is now unquestioned that the number of unit positive charges on the nucleus of any atom is given by the atomic number Z of the particular element. Thus the nuclear charge Q_n is given by the equation

$$Q_n = Ze \qquad (\text{I.5-5})$$

where e is the absolute magnitude of the charge on an electron. Also, then, Z must specify the number of electrons surrounding the nucleus. With this concept the few irregularities in Mendeleev's periodic table, based on atomic weights, were resolved.

In the hydrogen atom, then, the nucleus has a single positive charge and about it there moves one electron. The helium atom has a nucleus with two positive charges and two extranuclear electrons. Uranium, the 92nd element, has a nucleus with 92 unit positive charges and the same number of extranuclear electrons.

Since the lightest positively charged massive particle was the nucleus of the hydrogen atom, given the special name of *proton*, it was early assumed that atomic nuclei were built up of closely packed protons. The mass of the proton $(1.664 \times 10^{-24}$ gm) is approximately unity on the usual atomic weight scale (1.00812) and it carries a single positive charge. In order to account for the mass of a nucleus of mass number A, it was necessary to suppose it contained A protons. This would, of course, make the nuclear charge equal to Ae, rather than to Ze. It was therefore suggested by Bohr that $(A - Z)$ electrons, to counterbalance the excess nuclear charge $(A - Z)e$, were contained in the nucleus. These electrons would contribute a negligible amount of mass. This seemed reasonable, too, in virtue of the fact that electrons (beta particles) were emitted from some radioactive elements.

1.6. THE BOHR THEORY OF THE ATOM

According to Rutherford's hypothesis, then, an atom consists of a small, positively charged nucleus and a "cloud" of electrons, Z in number, surrounding it. Classical mechanics and electrodynamics could not account for the stability of such a system. An atom constructed in this fashion should lose energy continuously because the electrons, being accelerated in the Coulomb field of the nucleus, would emit electromagnetic radiation, ultimately resulting in the collapse of the atom. Such an expectation does not conform with the observed stability of atoms.

In 1913 N. Bohr, in an adaptation of Rutherford's ideas, introduced a revolutionary quantum theory of atomic structure to account for the well-defined lines exhibited in the spectra of atoms by combining Newtonian mechanics and the Planck quantum hypothesis. How can an atom produce a line spectrum? Bohr chose to disregard the constitution of the nucleus and to make the electrons moving around the nucleus the chief concern of the theory. He postulated that an atom would exist only in one of a number of discrete energy states (quantum states or stationary states), corresponding to particular, privileged circular orbits (referred to as stable or stationary[1] orbits) of the electrons around the nucleus. The atom was pictured as corresponding somewhat to a miniature solar system. The electrostatic attraction of the nucleus on the electrons played the part of the

---

[1]By *stationary* it is not meant to imply that the electrons are at rest; rather, it is meant that their orbits are stable and the motions are periodic, the energy of the system being constant.

sun's gravitational attraction on the planets. It was further postulated that such an atom could lose or gain energy only in transitions (quantum jumps) from one quantum state (or orbit) to another, instead of being able to emit or absorb energy continuously in accordance with classical theory. When moving in any one of the stable orbits, the electron could not radiate energy. This hypothesis thus rejected a large portion of the classical electrodynamical theory. The monochromatic radiation of frequency ν absorbed or emitted in such a transition between orbits was related to the energy difference ΔE between the two energy states or "energy levels" of the electron by means of the quantum relation

$$\Delta E = h\nu, \qquad (\text{I.6-1})$$

where h is Planck's constant (6.62×10^{-27} erg-sec). Again quite contrary to classical theory, the frequency of the emitted light is related to the energy change rather than to the frequency of the motion of the electron. The restrictions imposed by Bohr were extensions of the quantum assumptions introduced by Planck in 1900 in a totally different field of investigation — black-body radiation and incandescence — and by Einstein in the cases of the photoelectric effect and specific heats.

In considering the simplest atom, hydrogen, Bohr found that he could obtain remarkably good agreement with the observed, well-defined frequencies in the hydrogen spectrum if he assumed that the single electron was restricted to those orbits whose angular momenta were integral multiples of $h/2\pi$. The angular momentum of an electron of mass m and velocity v traveling in a circular orbit of radius a is mva. Therefore, Bohr's quantum condition for determining the allowed orbits is

$$mva = nh/2\pi, \qquad (\text{I.6-2})$$

where n is an integer called a *quantum number*. An additional condition, which follows from classical mechanics, is that the Coulomb attraction between the electron and the proton serves as the centripetal force on the electron moving in its circular orbit. Then, equating centripetal and centrifugal forces, there is obtained

$$\frac{e^2}{a^2} = \frac{mv^2}{a}. \qquad (\text{I.6-3})$$

By eliminating v from Equations I.6-2 and I.6-3 there is obtained

$$a = n^2h^2/4\pi^2me^2. \qquad (\text{I.6-4})$$

Thus the radius of each Bohr orbit of the electron is characterized by the so-called principal quantum number n. In the lowest, or normal, energy state of the hydrogen atom, $n = 1$, and the radius of the orbit of the electron is

$$h^2/4\pi^2me^2 \cong 0.5 \times 10^{-8} \text{ cm,}$$

reasonably close to the accepted value for the normal radius of the hydrogen atom.

The kinetic energy T of the electron is given by $\frac{1}{2}mv^2$, or, using Equation I.6-3 for an electron moving in a circular orbit of radius a

$$T = e^2/2a. \tag{I.6-5}$$

The potential energy V of the electron is this orbit, referred to the energy of the electron at infinity as the zero of energy, is

$$V = -e^2/a. \tag{I.6-6}$$

Thus the total energy E of the electron is

$$E = T + V \tag{I.6-7}$$

$$= -e^2/2a,$$

or, using Equation I.6-4,

$$E = -2\pi^2me^4/n^2h^2. \tag{I.6-8}$$

If an electron drops from an orbit with quantum number j to one of quantum number n, the energies being E_j and E_n, respectively, the Bohr assumption (I.6-1) gives

$$h\nu = E_n - E_j$$

$$= \frac{2\pi^2me^4}{h^2}\left(\frac{1}{n^2} - \frac{1}{j^2}\right). \tag{I.6-9}$$

The whole situation is summed up neatly by the use of an *energy diagram*, in which horizontal lines are plotted as ordinates proportional to the energies of the atom in its various quantized states. The state of zero energy (the ionized atom with the missing electron at rest at infinity) is placed near the top. Fig. I.6-1 is such a diagram for hydrogen. A spectral line results from the transition of the electron from one energy level to another. Accordingly, this line is represented in Fig. I.6-1 by a vertical line joining the two levels.

The Bohr theory was spectacularly successful in accounting for the main features of the hydrogen spectrum and of the spectra of hydrogenlike ions, in which all the electrons but one have been removed. When applied to the spectra of more complex elements, however, no quantitative agreement was obtainable.

A series of refinements was introduced. The motion of the nucleus was taken into account, together with the additional complication of the variation of the mass of the electron in accordance with the special theory of relativity. Elliptical orbits were introduced, giving rise to a second quantum number. A third quantum number had to be introduced to explain the splitting of the spectral lines into several closely spaced components under the influence of a magnetic field (the Zeeman effect) or of an electric field (the Stark effect). Finally, the concept of *electron spin* (a concept in which the electron, considered as a spherical shell of electricity, performs what can best be described mechanically as a

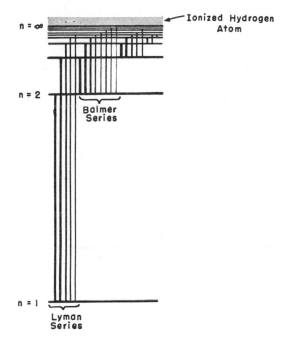

$n = \infty$

Ionized Hydrogen
Atom

$n = 2$

Balmer
Series

$n = 1$

Lyman
Series

FIG. I.6-1. *The energy diagram of a hydrogen atom.*

rotation about an axis through its center), originally proposed by Uhlenbeck and Goudsmit, together with a fourth quantum condition, was introduced to account for the so-called fine structure of spectra. Even when all these changes were made, however, Bohr's theory was unable to predict with precision the phenomena actually observed.

About 1925, Davisson and Germer conducted a famous experiment in which they caused electrons to be reflected from a crystal of nickel. They found that certain well-defined beams of electrons issued from the target for a certain definite incident angle, much as X rays were reflected from crystals. In other words, the beam behaved as if the electrons, all traveling in the same direction with the same velocity, possessed a perfectly definite wavelength.

These results could be explained in terms of a theory proposed in 1924 by L. de Broglie, in which particles of matter were assumed to be intrinsically wavelike as well as corpuscular in nature. De Broglie pointed out that this satisfied Bohr's quantum condition (I.6-2) if it were assumed that an electron of mass m and velocity v had associated with it a wave of wavelength

$$\lambda = h/mv \qquad \text{(I.6-10)}$$

and that the circumference of the orbit must be an integral multiple of λ. This theory was developed by Schrödinger, Heisenberg, and others into quantum mechanics.

The picture of an atom presented by Bohr is nearly, but not quite, in accord with modern views. It is not possible to give any precise mechanical picture of the motions of the electrons around the positively charged nucleus of an atom. The electron in a hydrogen atom does not move in a definite orbit, but rather in a somewhat random way, so that it is sometimes very close to the nucleus and sometimes far away. The electron travels all about the nucleus. By moving around rapidly, the electron effectively occupies all the space within a radius of about 1 Å (= 1×10^{-8} cm) of the nucleus and so gives the hydrogen atom an effective diameter of about 2Å. The speed of the electron is not constant, but its root-mean-square average speed is about 2×10^8 cm/sec. Thus the free hydrogen atom can be described as having a heavy nucleus at the center of a vague sphere defined by the space filled by the fast-moving electron in its motion about the nucleus. For other atoms each individual electron moves in the field resulting from the attraction of the nucleus and the repulsion of the other electrons, all of which are in motion; this is quite different from the behavior of the planets in the solar system, which move approximately independently of each other.

I.7. THE NEUTRON

The discovery of the neutron in 1932 is attributed to Sir James Chadwick. It was found by previous workers that a nonionizing radiation was emitted when light elements (particularly boron and beryllium) were bombarded by alpha particles from polonium (see Fig. I.7-1). When this radiation fell upon paraffin sheets (or other substances rich in hydrogen), a stream of high-speed protons

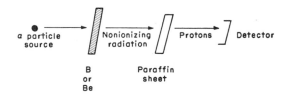

FIG. I.7-1. *Schematic arrangement of the apparatus that led to the discovery of the neutron.*

appeared. At first it was thought that gamma rays were generated by the alpha-particle bombardment. However, Chadwick showed that gamma rays of the energy required to eject protons from the paraffin could not be formed; unlike gamma radiation, this unknown radiation traveled at about one-tenth the speed of light. Rather, Chadwick surmised that the radiation consisted of energetic, neutral particles which he properly called neutrons.

Neutrons are particles whose mass (1.67454×10^{-24} gm or 1.008986 on the isotopic weight scale) is only slightly greater than that of the hydrogen atom and whose electric charge is zero. Because of this electrical neutrality, the neutron cannot be deflected by a magnetic or electric field. Hence indirect methods had to be employed to determine its mass. The neutron is not a stable form of matter, at least in the free state.

A nucleus composed of protons and electrons, such as is considered in § I.5, presented many difficulties which could not be satisfactorily resolved. For example, the electron was too large to be in the small space available to the nucleus; again, why did not the positive and negative charges annihilate each other? With the discovery of the neutron, the electron could be rejected from consideration as a nuclear particle, and the neutron could be substituted. It is believed today that the electrons emitted during beta decay are created during the decay process itself, just as radiation may be created and emitted when changes take place in the outer electronic configuration of an atom.

In a nucleus composed of protons and neutrons (these particles are called generically *nucleons*), the number of nucleons will be equal to the mass number A. (It would be, perhaps, better to use the term "nucleon number" for A rather than "mass number.") The number of protons will be given by the atomic number Z, since the charge on the nucleus is entirely due to protons. Thus the number of neutrons N is given by $A - Z$. The quantity $N - Z = A - 2Z$ represents the difference between the number of neutrons and protons in a nucleus and is referred to as the *neutron excess*.

Instead of a helium nucleus being composed of 4 protons and 2 electrons, it is now supposed to consist of 2 protons and 2 neutrons. The lithium-7 nucleus contains 3 protons and 4 neutrons; and so on for the other elements. Isotopes differ by the number of neutrons contained in the nuclei; the number of protons remains the same. Thus, in contrast to lithium-7, the nucleus of lithium-6 consists of 3 protons and 3 neutrons. (Nuclei of equal N but unequal Z are called *isotones*.)

I.8. BINDING ENERGIES OF NUCLEI

Much can be learned about the basic problems of nuclear structure by measurements of masses. Data on isotopic weights establish that the masses of nuclides are not equal to the sum of the masses of the nucleons that are supposed to compose them. For example, two neutrons plus two hydrogen atoms have a mass of 4.034262 instead of 4.003873 as is found for helium-4. These *mass defects* for the various nuclides were recognized as analogous to the heats of formation of chemical compounds and were attributable to the energy liberated when the elementary nuclear constituents are combined.

If protons and neutrons are assumed to be the elementary constituents of all nuclei, the mass defect of the nucleus is given by

$$\Delta M = ZM_p + NM_n - M', \tag{I.8-1}$$

where M_p, M_n, and M' are the masses, respectively, of the proton, neutron, and the nucleus under consideration. If the masses of the Z electrons are introduced, Equation I.8-1 becomes

$$\Delta M = Z(M_p + m_e) + NM_n - (M' + Zm_e) \qquad (I.8\text{-}2)$$

$$= ZM_H + NM_n - M$$

$$= ZM_H + (A - Z)M_n - M$$

$$= AM_n - Z(M_n - M_H) - M,$$

where M_H and M are the atomic masses of the neutral hydrogen atom and of the atom in question. Since A represents the number of nucleons in a nucleus, the mass defect per nucleon is

$$\frac{\Delta M}{A} = M_n - \frac{Z}{A}(M_n - M_H) - \frac{M}{A} \qquad (I.8\text{-}3)$$

$$= (M_n - 1) - \frac{Z}{A}(M_n - M_H) - \frac{M - A}{A}.$$

Thus the mass defect of 0.030389 mass unit found above for helium-4 becomes a mass defect per nucleon (four in number) of 0.007597 mass unit.

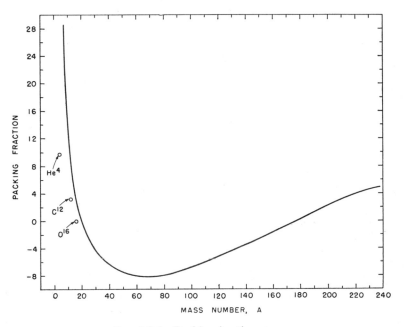

FIG. I.8-1. *Packing fraction curve.*

In "pre-neutron" days, Aston expressed his results in terms of the so-called *packing fraction P*, defined by the equation

$$P = \frac{M - A}{A} \times 10^4. \tag{I.8-4}$$

Curves of P vs. A are called packing fraction curves (see Fig. I.8-1). For oxygen-16, by definition $M - A = 0$ and hence also is the packing fraction. For other elements the packing fraction may be positive or negative. It will be noted that P has a minimum value of about -8.4 in the vicinity of iron, cobalt, and nickel. If Equation I.8-4 is introduced into Equation I.8-3 there results

$$\frac{\Delta M}{A} = (M_n - 1) - \frac{Z}{A}(M_n - M_H) - (P \times 10^{-4}) \tag{I.8-5}$$

$$= 0.008986 - 0.000841 \frac{Z}{A} - (P \times 10^{-4}).$$

Now Einstein in his theory of relativity demonstrated that the mass of a body is a measure of its energy content. When the energy of a body is changed, no matter what form the energy takes, the mass of the body will change, and vice versa. The governing equation is

$$\Delta E = (\Delta m)c^2, \tag{I.8-6}$$

where the change in mass, Δm, is the equivalent of the change in energy, ΔE, and c is the velocity of light. Equation I.8-6, often referred to as the Einstein *mass-energy equation*, is fundamental to the whole subject of nuclear energy. Numerically,

$$\Delta E = (\Delta m) \times (2.998 \times 10^{10} \text{ cm/sec})^2 \tag{I.8-7}$$

$$= (\Delta m) \times 8.99 \times 10^{20} \text{ cm}^2/\text{sec}^2,$$

if ΔE is in ergs and Δm in grams. In atomic studies it has become the practice to express energies in units of *electron volts* (ev), rather than in ergs. The electron volt is the energy acquired by any particle carrying a unit (electronic) charge when it falls through a potential of one volt:

$$1 \text{ ev} = 1.603 \times 10^{-12} \text{ erg}. \tag{I.8-8}$$

For convenience, the kiloelectron volt (1 kev $\equiv 10^3$ ev) and the million electron volt (1 Mev $\equiv 10^6$ ev) are often employed. Using the relationship of Equation I.8-8, Equation I.8-7 becomes

$$\Delta E \text{ (in ev)} = 5.61 \times 10^{32} (\Delta m)(\text{in grams}) \tag{I.8-9}$$

$$= 9.31 \times 10^8 (\Delta m)(\text{in atomic mass units})$$

or

$$\Delta E \text{ (in Mev)} = 931 (\Delta m) \text{ (in atomic mass units).} \tag{I.8-10}$$

Thus 1 atomic mass unit is equivalent to 931 Mev. The energy equivalent of the mass of an electron is 0.511 Mev.

For chemical reactions the difference in mass corresponding to the heat change involved is so small as to be outside the limits of measurement with present techniques. For example, consider a chemical reaction (such as $C + O_2 \rightarrow CO_2$) in which about

$$100{,}000 \text{ calories} = 418 \times 10^{10} \text{ ergs}$$

of energy are liberated. This energy corresponds to a mass change of

$$\Delta m = \frac{418 \times 10^{10} \text{ ergs}}{8.99 \times 10^{20} \text{ ergs/gm}}$$
$$= 4.6 \times 10^{-9} \text{ gm.}$$

The mass-energy changes involved in nuclear processes, however, are of such a magnitude that the changes of mass are measurable.

When expressed in terms of its energy equivalent, the mass defect per nucleon represents a tightness of binding and is a measure of the stability of the element. The mass defect itself represents the mass which would appear in the form of energy in the hypothetical process of assembling a particular atom from the requisite number of nucleons and electrons. The same amount of energy would, of course, have to be supplied to the atom in order to break it up into its constituent particles. The energy equivalent of the mass defect is called the *binding energy*. For the helium-4 atom the binding energy is (0.030389 amu)(931 Mev/amu) = 28.3 Mev. The binding energy per nucleon is therefore 7.08 Mev. From Equations I.8-5 and I.8-10

$$\text{Binding Energy per nucleon (in Mev)} = 8.3666 - 0.783\frac{Z}{A} - 931(P \times 10^{-4}).$$

$$(\text{I.8-11})$$

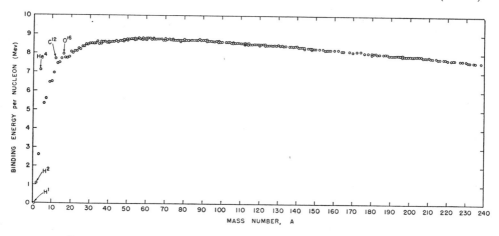

FIG. I.8-2. *The binding energy per nucleon as a function of mass number.*

In Fig. I.8-2 the binding energies per nucleon for various elements throughout the periodic table are shown graphically. For elements of atomic weight greater than 20, the values vary only slightly from about 8 Mev, reaching a maximum of 8.7 Mev at atomic weights around 70 and decreasing slowly to about 7.6 Mev/nucleon for the heaviest elements. Evidently the nuclei in the middle of the periodic table are the most strongly bound.

From Fig. I.8-2 it may be seen that, if it were possible to convert some elements into others by rearrangements of the nucleons, energy could be released. The maximum binding energy per nucleon occurs in nuclei which have mass numbers about 60–70. In heavier nuclei, the total binding energy of the A nucleons can be increased by dividing the original nucleus into two smaller nuclei. Thus, if uranium-238 is divided into two nuclei, each having a mass number of $\frac{1}{2}(238) = 119$, the binding energy per nucleon will increase from about 7.6 to 8.5 Mev/nucleon. This is an increase of 0.9 Mev/nucleon, or some 210 Mev for the division of the single uranium-238 nucleus. This phenomenon of *fission*, in which a heavy nucleus breaks into two or more medium heavy fragments, forms the basis of the practical utilization of nuclear energy.

It is equally apparent that if the intermediate elements could be synthesized from the very light isotopes, then an enormous release of energy per nucleon would result. Such a process is termed *fusion*, as opposed to fission.

CHAPTER II

DETECTION OF RADIATION

II.1. IONIZATION BY NUCLEAR RADIATIONS

Nuclear radiations are rapidly becoming a part of everyday life. They are not detectable by use of our senses. Special apparatus is required to tell how much and what kind of radiation is present.

The detection of nuclear radiations is based on the fact that a charged particle passing through matter leaves along its path a string of ionized or excited atoms or molecules which can be detected and counted. In general, neutral particles, such as neutrons and gamma-ray photons, do not produce ionization or excitation directly, but they can produce charged particles as the result of their interactions with matter and thus provide a means of detection. In any event, charged particles can be subjected to the actions of electric and magnetic fields, can promote or induce chemical or nuclear reactions, can cause the emission of light, and so forth, by means of which detection is possible.

The majority of present-day detectors are based on the ionization produced by the passage of a charged particle through a gas. As a result of inelastic collisions, with a resultant transfer of energy from the moving particle to the molecules of the gas, a number of ion pairs, i.e., positively charged gaseous ions and free electrons, are produced. In general, there is a close proportionality between the number of ion pairs formed and the total loss of energy by the incident particle. Experimentally it has been found that the number of ion pairs formed does not appear to depend markedly on the velocity or charge of the particle. The average amount of energy lost in the production of one pair in various gases is generally around 30 to 35 ev.

After the ionization process has been completed, electrons and ions will move in a random fashion. Unless they are separated by an external electric field, they will recombine. The originally free electrons often attach themselves to neutral gas molecules and thereby form negative heavy ions. The probability of this process depends very strongly on the energy of the electron and the nature of the gas.

In its passage through a stopping medium, a primary beta ray will liberate secondary electrons from the atoms. For example, Fig. II.1-1 is a picture representing the passage of an electron through a gas. Although the atoms of the gas are electrically neutral, the Coulomb interaction between the moving electron and the charged constituents of the atom produce a deflection. Such elastic collisions, which do not result in the transfer of energy between the electron and the internal structure of the atom, are indicated for atoms A, B, C; the moving electron imparts a small fraction of its kinetic energy to the gaseous atoms. It may happen that a very close encounter with an atom, as at D, occurs, and there is an extremely powerful repulsion between the moving electron and an atomic electron such that sufficient energy is imparted to the latter to excite it or even to cause its ejection from the atom. The predominant mechanism for energy losses is by means of such inelastic collisions. An electron may lose a large fraction of its energy in one such collision.

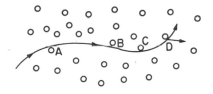

FIG. II.1-1. *Schematic representation of the path of an electron in a gas.*

There are two ways by which an energetic, heavy, charged particle, such as an alpha, produces the ionization which dissipates its energy and velocity in its passage through matter. In the primary collision with the electrons in an atom, the most probable of the ionizing collisions are those in which a relatively slow secondary electron is ejected with kinetic energy smaller than the energy necessary to cause ionization. These electrons may attach themselves to neutral atoms, forming negative ions. A small fraction of the ionizing collisions, however, produces secondary electrons of relatively high energy (perhaps several kev) called delta rays. The delta rays themselves then go on to produce further ionization in the atoms of the stopping material, leading to secondary ionization and losing energy just as any electrons of this energy would. The *total ionization* is the sum of the *primary ionization* and this *secondary ionization*.

The most remarkable experimental facts about the total ionization are that the energy loss per ion pair formed is very nearly independent of the energy of the primary charged particle and is also nearly the same for alpha particles, protons, electrons, etc. Taking 33 ev as the average energy loss per ion pair formed, it is seen that a particle with an energy of one Mev will be stopped completely when it has produced about 30,000 ion pairs.

The intensity of the ionization produced by a moving charged particle in its path through a gas is expressed by the *specific ionization*, that is, the number of ion pairs formed per unit length of path. For particles of the same mass the specific ionization increases with the magnitude of the charge. For particles of the same energy it increases with the mass (and hence with decreasing speed); this may be explained by the assumption that momentum changes are more probable since the more slowly moving particle spends more time in the vicinity of an atom or molecule, thereby increasing the chance of ionization.

Alpha particles from radioactive sources produce 50,000 to 100,000 ion pairs per centimeter of ordinary air. For alpha particles with energies in excess of about 1 Mev, the specific ionization is approximately proportional to the reciprocal of the velocity. A plot of specific ionization versus distance from the source is called a Bragg curve (see Fig. II.1-2). As the distance from the source increases, the relative specific ionization increases, at first quite slowly and then more rapidly. The maximum specific ionization is reached when the energy has decreased to about 370 kev. After that the specific ionization falls rapidly to zero.

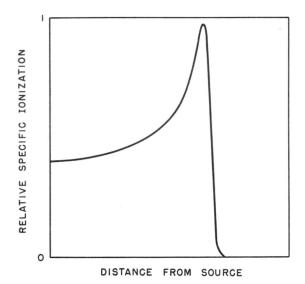

FIG. II.1-2. *Representation of a Bragg curve for an alpha particle.*

Beta particles of similar energy (4 to 10 Mev), having a higher speed and smaller charge, will leave no more than a few hundred ion pairs per centimeter. However, since the total path of the beta particle would be of the order of one hundred times that of the alpha particle, the difference in *total* ionization would not be very great.

Gamma rays and X rays ionize gases indirectly, by ejecting electrons with appreciable velocity. It is these rapidly moving, secondary electrons which produce ion pairs. The specific ionization of gamma radiation thus depends on the energy of the expelled electron. The specific ionization caused by a gamma ray is about one-hundredth of that caused by an electron possessing the same energy. At low energies the most important process of ionization by a gamma ray is through the photoelectric effect, in which a bound electron is ejected from the atom or molecule. The radiation completely disappears in this process, energy and momentum being transferred to the electron and the resultant ion. Since gamma rays are usually very energetic, their energy is large compared to the binding energy of the electron in the atom. Hence the kinetic energy of the ejected electron is not much less than that of the gamma radiation.

The loss of energy due to ionization by a fast charged particle is greater in a gaseous substance than for an equal mass of the same substance in a condensed state.

II.2. THE ELECTROSCOPE

The ordinary gold-leaf electroscope has played a major role in the study of radioactivity ever since Becquerel observed that the rays from uranium caused its discharge. In its simplest form, the instrument consists of a short, vertical metal rod with a metal sphere or plate at its upper end; to its lower end is attached a small, rectangular sheet of gold leaf. The rod is usually supported, with suitable insulation, in a box which serves to protect the delicate gold leaf from air currents.

If a gold-leaf electroscope is charged by means of a suitable applied potential, so that the movable leaf diverges from the fixed rod, a condition of equilibrium between electrostatic and gravitational forces will hold almost indefinitely. But if the air near the electroscope is ionized, the ions are attracted, neutralizing some of the charges, causing the leaf to change its position. The position of the leaf may be observed through a microscope of low magnification, with a scale in the eyepiece. The rate of collapse of the leaf towards the rod can be measured in terms of divisions on the scale per unit time, giving a measure of the ionization current which, in turn, is a measure of the rate at which ions are produced.

In the gold-leaf electroscope the force opposing deflection of the leaf is gravitation. In the quartz-fiber electroscope designed by Lauritsen the moving fiber, about 6 mm in length and 3 to 5 μ (1 μ = 10^{-4} cm) in diameter, is so thin and light that gravitation exerts virtually no effect on it. The elastic force of the quartz is used in place of gravitation as the restoring force, the advantages being

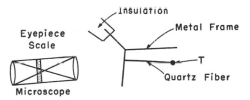

FIG. II.2-1. *Schematic representation of the Lauritsen electroscope.*

that it is possible to find an arrangement which will give a much more nearly linear scale than is found in the gold-leaf electroscope and the instrument is much more sensitive (about one hundred times). The heart of the instrument is illustrated in Fig. II.2-1. On the metal frame is attached a quartz fiber upon which gold has been spattered to render it conducting. A "T" is added, at right angles, on the end of the fiber to make it more easily visible in the microscope. A charge given to the system causes the fiber to bend away from the metal support. The presence of ions in the neighborhood will cause a neutralization of the charge and permits the fiber to return to its original position.

Electroscopes are generally used for relative measurements only. Alpha radiation is most easily detected, since the specific ionization is high. By placing a suitable alpha-ray absorber, such as a thin sheet of aluminum, over a radioactive sample, however, the ionization due to beta and gamma rays may be observed. Actually, since gamma rays produce ionization to a much less extent than do beta rays, the discharge of an electroscope in this case is caused almost entirely by the beta rays. To measure the activity due to gamma rays alone, the radioactive sample must be surrounded by a sufficient amount of material to absorb both alpha and beta rays.

Electroscopes are not sensitive enough to detect single particles. With a Lauritsen electroscope it has been possible to detect as few as ten electrons per minute.

II.3. THE CLOUD CHAMBER

A Wilson cloud chamber, one of the most widely known of the apparatuses for the detection of nuclear particles, renders the paths of ionizing particles graphically visible by the presence of a fog consisting of condensed droplets of water along the path of ionization. The principle involved depends on the observation by C. T. R. Wilson that ions can act as centers for the formation of condensed droplets in a supersaturated vapor, produced by the simple process of a rapid adiabatic expansion of a saturated vapor. The rapid (about $\frac{1}{30}$ second) expansion causes a fall in temperature to below the dew point, permitting the excess vapor to settle out in the form of liquid drops which appear as cloud or fog if ions are present. If the vapor is clean, particularly if it is free from dust, the state of supersaturation is maintained unless these ions are present, and it is the droplets which indicate the presence of the ions. By illuminating the vapor after the expansion has occurred, photographs can be taken to provide permanent records. Fig. II.3-1 is a sketch of Wilson's original cloud chamber.

One disadvantage of the instrument is that time (anywhere from 1 to 20 seconds) must elapse before the cloud chamber is ready for a second expansion. Automatic arrangements have been devised for rapid repetition of the expansion and the taking of photographs. Some success has been attained in the development of a "continuous" cloud chamber by means of a steady flow of gas against a vapor to produce a supersaturated state.

Because of low penetrating power, sources of alpha particles must be inside the cloud chamber. Beta rays may be sent into the apparatus through a thin window with little loss in energy. Gamma rays may be studied by observing the secondary electrons originating in the chamber. Neutrons can be studied by observing the recoil protons arising because of the impact of the neutrons on any

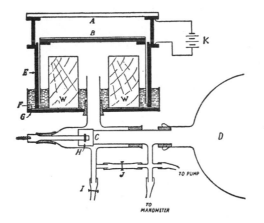

Fig. II.3-1. *Wilson's cloud chamber. Here AB is the expansion chamber, cylindrical in shape and completely enclosed. The movable base B slides inside the cylinder E and serves as a piston. The battery K provided the electric field to remove stray ions just before an expansion occurred.* [*Reprinted by permission from N. N. DasGupta and S. K. Ghosh, "A Report on the Wilson Cloud Chamber and Its Applications in Physics,"* Rev. Mod. Phys. 18: 255 (1946).]

hydrogenous material within the chamber, or from certain neutron-induced nuclear reactions.

In general, photographs of the thick tracks produced by alpha rays show that the particles travel in straight lines. Near the ends of their paths, when the speeds have been greatly diminished, the particles (about 1 in 100) are liable to suffer deflection, presumably as the result of impacts with the nuclei in the vapor. The particles seem to have a well-defined mean range or distance of travel.

By counting the drops in a cloud track, the specific ionization can be determined and the nature of the particle identified. The cloud-chamber method is the only one that permits a separate determination of the primary and total ionization. The alpha particle has the highest specific ionization and gives a short, dense track. A beta particle leaves a thin track that is diffuse and tortuous. The number of collisions of a beta particle with the molecules of a medium increases as it slows down; hence the path of a slow beta appears curved because of a great number of random deflections.

If a magnetic field is applied perpendicular to the velocity of the particle being photographed, the path is circular. By measuring the radius of curvature of the track, the momentum and energy of the particle can be determined.

II.4. THE IONIZATION CHAMBER

If the electric field across a contained volume of gas is small enough so that the ions and electrons formed by nuclear radiation do not gain sufficient energy between collisions to produce additional ionization, we are dealing with an ionization chamber. The ion pairs formed by each entering ionizing particle should be collected at the electrodes and produce a pulse of charge (or voltage) which may be counted. The magnitude of this pulse will depend on the number of ion pairs formed and collected. The time taken to collect both positive ions and electrons can be made to be of the order of 10^{-4} second, depending on the applied potential, the dimensions of the chamber, and the pressure and ionization characteristics of the gas. Because of their mass, the positive ions are collected some thousands of times more slowly than are the electrons. The shape of the pulse is thus something like that illustrated in Fig. II.4-1. The initial steep rise is caused by the rapid motion of the electrons; the much slower rise is due to the motion of the ions. Provided that new ion tracks are not formed in the gas more quickly than the ions are collected (for then the two pulses would be counted as one), a series of charge or voltage pulses will be obtained corresponding to the number of ionizing particles passing through the chamber.

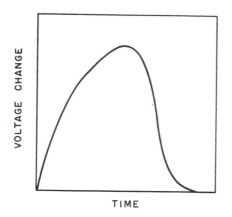

FIG. II.4-1. *Schematic representation of a pulse from an ionization chamber.*

If the particle flux is so great that ions are produced more or less continuously, the chamber output is a steady current rather than a series of discrete pulses. The essential differences between various instruments using these principles are in the nature of the current-measuring systems.

If the electric field in the ionization chamber is comparatively small, the electrons may have time to form negative ions before being collected, and losses due to recombination between the slowly moving positive and negative ions, particularly within densely ionized tracks, may occur. Thus, for a given ionization caused by the passage of a charged particle, the ionization current flowing in a circuit of which the chamber is a part (see Fig. II.4-2) increases with increasing voltage from the battery, but eventually shows saturation when recombination becomes negligible. The value of the electrical field strength at which saturation is reached will depend markedly on the gas, its purity, and the specific ionization of the particle. Even for a

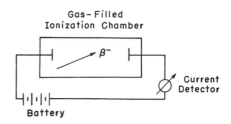

FIG. II.4-2. *Schematic representation of an ionization chamber.*

small average ionization, large fields might be required if the individual tracks show a high density of ions. If the field strength is sufficiently increased, secondary ionization can occur, even before saturation is reached.

A sensitive electrometer can detect a charge of 10^{-16} coulomb, which is about the quantity of electricity of either sign produced by about 60,000 ion pairs. It is thus possible to detect the charge produced by an electron in ionizing a gas *directly*. A simple circuit is shown schematically in Fig. II.4-3. When the

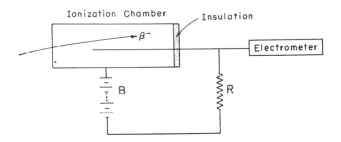

FIG. II.4-3. *Simple type of ionization chamber.*

electron (or other ionizing particle) enters the ionization chamber, ions are formed. The ionization chamber contains two electrodes (in this instance the outer case and an insulated central rod) between which an electric field is applied by the battery B through a high resistance R. The ions formed by the fast electron are separated by the electric field, and the positive ions are driven to the central electrode, whose potential rises when it receives the charge. The resultant change of potential is indicated by the electrometer.

For practical purposes an electrometer is seldom used, for it is far from rugged and requires skill and experience to set up and keep in operation. The period of a sensitive electrometer is long, so that several seconds must elapse between the detection of nuclear particles.

Instruments of another type use ionization chambers in conjunction with electronic amplifiers. As schematically indicated in Fig. II.4-4, the ionization current may be made to flow through a high resistance R, and the voltage

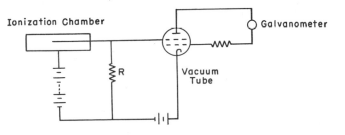

FIG. II.4-4. *Ionization chamber with DC amplifier.*

developed is applied to the central grid of a vacuum tube (the General Electric pliotron FP54 or the Victoreen VX41A, for example, is suitable) and measured in terms of the plate current by a galvanometer. Additional stages of amplification may be employed.

II.5. THE PROPORTIONAL COUNTER

If the electric field in an ionization chamber is sufficiently raised and if the electrons do not recombine with positive ions or form negative ions, an increase of the ionization current is observed at about the saturation value for complete collection of the ion pairs. This condition is best attained by using a cylindrical chamber, which acts as the negative electrode (cathode), and a central wire as the positive electrode (anode). The field is then very strong in the neighborhood of the central wire and falls off rapidly with distance.

The increase in the ionization current sets in as soon as the electrons gain sufficient energy in the electric field to ionize neutral gas molecules in collisions. The electrons resulting from this secondary ionization may in turn cause further ionization; every primary ionizing event thus causes an avalanche of secondary ionization. If n ion pairs were formed initially by the entrance into the chamber of an ionizing particle then, when the avalanche has stopped, mn electrons and mn positive ions will have been formed, mostly in the space very close to the central wire. The number m is called the multiplication factor. (For the ionization chamber, $m = 1$.) This phenomenon is used to amplify the effects of weakly ionizing radiations.

Now in the process of the formation of the avalanche, electromagnetic radiation of high energy is emitted by the molecules excited by electron impact or as a result of recombination. Under suitable conditions, this radiation can release photoelectrons at the negative electrode or from components of the gas having a lower ionization potential than the component which emitted the light. The light might therefore contribute to the secondary ionization and spread the discharge over the whole volume of the ionization chamber. However, as long as the number of photoelectrons formed by the secondary electrons is small, the detector is called a proportional counter, since the total number of secondaries is proportional to the total number of primary ion pairs if every primary electron actually multiplies by the same number m. This will occur as long as space charges due to the secondary positive ions do not materially change the electric field and the primary ionization does not occur close to the central positive electrode.

The advantage of the proportional counter is that the size or height of the pulse produced by a single particle may be increased enormously (by as much as 10^4). The greater the multiplication factor, the less is the needed gain in the amplifier or the less is the sensitivity needed in the recording equipment. The instrument can detect much smaller initial ionization than is possible with the ionization chamber. A disadvantage of operation is the need for great stabilization of the applied voltage, since any change will alter the gas amplification and hence the output.

The pulse can be registered by means of a sensitive electrometer or, in conjunction with amplifying equipment, can be used to operate a mechanical or electronic counter. Because of the proportional character of the amplification, varying as the number of primary ion pairs and hence with the energy of the primary ionizing particle, an alpha particle will give a larger pulse than will a beta particle or a gamma ray, just as in the ionization chamber. By means of suitable electronic devices the smaller pulses can be ignored and alpha particles counted in the presence of beta and gamma rays.

The total time for one pulse is about 5×10^{-5} second, mainly arising from the relatively slower motions of the positive ions, and this limits the repetition rate for a proportional counter. The pulse shape of a proportional counter is quite different from that observed when the counter is operated as an ionization chamber. When the primary ions are not all produced at the same place, but are distributed along a track of finite length, the electrons from the various sections of the track will reach the region where gas multiplication occurs at various times. This modifies the shape of the initial part of the pulse in a manner that depends on the position and orientation of the track. For a reasonably high multiplication factor, however, the voltage pulses caused by an ionizing event will be of the same height, irrespective of the position of the ionizing track, unless the track is located within a few mean free paths of the electrons from the central wire.

In practice it is noticed that the height of the pulse caused by the same primary ionization will show a certain spread, arising from various causes. In the first place the number of ion pairs produced by the primary particle shows a certain fluctuation and, similarly, the subsequent multiplication shows additional statistical variations. An additional spread of the pulse height is encountered if the electrons undergo capture in their paths to the collecting electrode; since the probability for formation of a negative ion depends on the number of collisions which the electron undergoes, the pulse size will vary according to the location of the primary ionization. In addition, ionization tracks may not be completely inside the active volume of the chamber.

II.6. THE GEIGER-MULLER COUNTER

If the negative potential of the outer electrode of a cylindrical proportional counter is raised so that the multiplication factor becomes very large, the pulses gradually lose proportionality to the primary ionization. If the voltage is raised still further, the pulses eventually become the same size, independent of the magnitude of the primary ionization. The counter then operates as a Geiger-Müller (G-M) counter. The photoelectrons generated in the avalanche (see

§ II.5) play an important part. Their action consists in spreading the discharge from the region of primary ionization throughout the whole volume of the counter, thereby producing the large pulses independently of the primary ionization. The gas-amplification factor may attain a value as high as 10^8, so that pulses are obtained which require little external amplification.

The electrons reach the central wire anode in a very short time. The positive ions move much more slowly toward the walls of the tube, which act as the cathode. As a result, a positive space charge is built up near the anode; the effective potential difference in its vicinity is consequently decreased and the discharge is terminated.

One of the troublesome features of the G-M counter is that when an ionizing particle produces an avalanche the resulting discharge pulse is liable to continue for some time. If another ionizing particle enters the counter tube before the discharge is complete, the pulse it should produce will be confused with the preceding one, and so on for subsequent pulses. In other words, the separate pulses are not resolved. The continuation of the discharge or, more correctly, the formation of a multiple discharge, appears to be due to the positive members of the ion pairs. When they reach the cathode the positive ions cause electrons to be liberated; these move rapidly toward the central wire and thus renew the discharge previously terminated, as described above.

There are two distinctly different types of Geiger-Müller counters: the non-self-quenching and the self-quenching types. In the latter the filling gas is a mixture of argon and a few per cent of a polyatomic organic gas or vapor (such as methane, ethane, or ethyl alcohol) or a halogen gas. The argon permits a high specific ionization and a low starting potential (the voltage at which counts are first observed), while the organic molecules quench the discharge. A collision between an argon ion and the organic molecule generally results in an electron transfer, leaving the argon neutral and the organic molecule positively charged. Further, the energy of the positive argon ions, which would otherwise have caused the emission of the troublesome electrons from the cylinder walls, may be utilized in decomposing the organic molecules. (In addition, the organic compound also absorbs, with fair efficiency, the high-energy radiation; this may lead to dissociation rather than to ionization of the organic molecule, thereby preventing the production of photoelectrons.) The disappearance of the organic compound sets a limit to the life of the self-quenching counter, but a good tube may be used for as many as 10^8 to 10^9 pulses before becoming inoperative.

The quenching of the discharge in the non-self-quenching type is accomplished by means of an external resistance or by the use of an auxiliary electronic circuit. These automatically reduce the voltage below the starting potential after each pulse and then restore it in time for the next pulse. However, the maximum useful counting rate is seriously reduced below that for the self-quenching counter.

When properly quenched, a G-M counter will have a recovery (or resolving) time of about 2×10^{-4} second. Thus, if particles enter at a uniform rate, a maximum of 5000 per second could be counted.

Because the pulse size is essentially independent of the number of primary ion pairs, the G-M counter cannot distinguish between alpha and beta or other ionizing particles. If, however, alphas are present, they can easily be prevented from entering the counter by means of thin sheets of absorbing material.

The pulses of Geiger-Müller counters show variable delays between the occurrence of the primary ionization and the time at which the voltage pulse is built up to a certain height. This delay is caused partly by the finite time which the primary ionization electrons need to travel to the inner electrode and partly by the different time which the discharge requires to spread over the counter. Consequently the time lag will vary with the position of the primary ionization, in the radial as well as in the axial direction.

II.7. SCINTILLATION COUNTERS

When ionizing particles pass through certain crystals, called phosphors, fluorescent radiation, characteristic of the material of the crystal, is emitted. In the early days of nuclear physics detection of particles by observation through a microscope of the individual flashes of fluorescent light, called scintillations, from ZnS crystals containing a trace of copper, was widely used. The work was extremely laborious, and although it permitted a direct determination of the number of alpha particles emitted by a radioactive substance in unit time, the method fell into disuse. However, recently it has been possible to record single scintillations by means of a photomultiplier tube. It has been found that the light from crystals of naphthalene, anthracene, and phenanthrene and of sodium and potassium iodides containing traces of thallium, for example, will excite a photocathode when ionizing radiations enter.

The action is as follows. The charged particle, in plowing through the crystal, produces ionization and breaks chemical bonds. A fair fraction of the recovery process takes the form of the return of electrons with attendant emission of light. This light causes the ejection of one or more photoelectrons from the sensitive cathode of the photomultiplier. These electrons are accelerated by an electric field to the next electrode, whose surface is such that the impingement of the accelerated electron produces several slow electrons. These, in turn, are accelerated to the next electrode, and so on through many stages, until a considerable avalanche reaches the last electrode and a readily measurable current pulse is produced. The process is illustrated in Fig II.7-1.

The scintillating crystal is usually placed close to the window of the photomultiplier tube in order to ensure the collection of as much light as possible on the photocathode. However, if it is desired to operate the multiplier at a distance

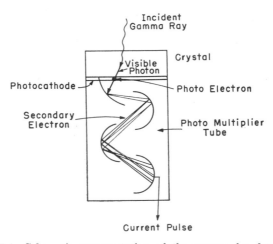

FIG. II.7-1. *Schematic representation of the process for detecting and measuring a gamma ray with crystal and photomultiplier tube.*

from the crystal (for example, in the presence of a magnetic field), the light may be "piped" to the tube through glass or Lucite rods.

One of the outstanding features of the scintillation counter is its extremely short resolving time; with suitable fast amplifiers, response times of the order of 2×10^{-8} second are possible with inorganic crystals and as little as 10^{-9} second with certain plastics and organic liquids, permitting very rapid counting. The delivered pulse is roughly proportional to the energy of the ionizing particle or photon, thus affording a means of distinguishing between kinds of radiation, which a Geiger counter cannot do. The instrument can be made very sensitive to gamma radiation. Further, by suitable electronic biasing of associated amplifier circuits, it is possible to count only those pulses whose heights exceed some preset value.

One of the weaknesses of scintillators using organic materials has been the relatively low atomic numbers of their constituent elements. Improvements have been made by the development of scintillating organic compounds which incorporate such heavy elements as lead or mercury.

II.8. PHOTOGRAPHIC DETECTION

Until the development of electrical counting instruments, photographic emulsions constituted one of the most important tools in the study of radiations from radioactive substances. Recent improvements in the preparation of emulsions have made their use important once again.

Like the cloud chamber, the photographic plate can register the occurrence of an ionizing particle by recording the ionization along its path. A track, containing a number of developable silver halide grains, is produced in the emulsion and has an appearance very much like those of cloud-chamber pictures. The number of developable grains is always very much smaller than the number of ion pairs created along the track. However, if the specific ionization is low enough, the grain density is still proportional to the specific energy loss. For high specific ionization the number of developable grains becomes constant, simply because every grain in the path of the particle is rendered developable.

The pictures produced can be used to furnish information about the energy of the particle, the direction of propagation, the point of origin, and so on. In principle the identification of a particle can be made from its range in the emulsion and the grain density of the track if the grains appear resolved.

The great advantages which the photographic plate offers as compared with the cloud chamber are that the emulsion has a stopping power and a reaction probability corresponding to a very large volume of gas (since it consists of solid materials) and it is permanently sensitive, not restricted to rather infrequently repeated short intervals as is the cloud chamber. On the other hand, the tedious ness of the work detracts from the convenience of the photographic method. Further, no specific events can be selected, as can be done, for instance, with counter-controlled cloud-chamber expansions.

II.9. CHERENKOV COUNTERS

The speed v of a charged particle of high energy traversing a transparent medium of index of refraction n considerably greater than unity may be very close to that of light in free space ($n = 1$), namely, $c = 3 \times 10^{10}$ cm/sec. On the other hand, the velocity of light in the transparent medium, and hence the velocity of the electromagnetic disturbances associated with the moving charge, can travel in the medium only with a speed V given by the expression

$$V = c/n. \tag{II.9-1}$$

Thus it is possible actually to have a charged particle moving in a substance with a velocity exceeding the local velocity of light. This is not in conflict in any way with the special theory of relativity, which merely assumes that the velocity of the charged particle cannot exceed the velocity of light *in free space*.

It was predicted by Cherenkov in 1934 and subsequently verified experimentally that in such instances the moving charge would emit some of its energy as visible radiation. This was substantiated theoretically by Frank and Tamm in 1937. At each point in the medium, the moving charge produces an electromagnetic disturbance which is propagated from that point in the form of a light wave. This radiation shows an extremely pronounced spatial asymmetry, being sent only in a forward direction which forms a definite angle with the direction of the exciting source, whereas the ordinary phenomena associated with luminescence are spherically symmetrical. The angle θ between the emitted radiation and the path of the moving particle is such that

$$\cos \theta = V/v = \frac{(c/n)}{v} = \frac{c}{nv}. \qquad \text{(II.9-2)}$$

In other directions the waves cancel as a result of interference. The emitted wave front is much like the shock wave in an elastic medium traversed by a ballistic projectile moving at supersonic speeds (Mach waves) or to the bow wave produced by a boat. The blue glow observed in the water of a reactor, close to the active fuel elements, is just this *Cherenkov radiation*.

It follows from Equation II.9-2, since the value of a cosine cannot exceed unity, that the appearance of the radiation is possible only under the condition that $vn > c$. Thus the effect primarily depends only on the speed v of the charged particle, not upon its momentum or energy. As a consequence, there exists a threshold velocity, v_{th}, determined by the condition

$$v_{th} = c/n, \qquad \text{(II.9-3)}$$

for the appearance of the radiation, and a corresponding threshold energy.

It might be expected that the Cherenkov radiation would be completely masked by radiation emitted in a medium as a result of recombination of ion pairs after ionization caused by the moving charged particle. The threshold effect and the directional characteristics, however, allow the radiation to be uniquely identified. Although the intensity of the radiation is quite small, a significant portion of this light can reach the cathode of a photomultiplier in a properly arranged experimental apparatus, which thus acts as a counter (similar to the scintillation counter) in which the radiation emitted by the particle serves directly for its measurement. Of course, slow particles below the threshold energy cannot be detected.

CHAPTER III

THE NUCLEAR PARTICLES

III.1. THE RADIOACTIVE DISINTEGRATION LAW

With the object of correlating the perplexing facts of radioactivity (see § I.4), in 1902 Rutherford and Soddy proposed a theory of *radioactive disintegration*. They suggested that the atoms of radioelements, unlike those of stable species, undergo a spontaneous disintegration with the emission of alpha or beta particles, thereby forming atoms of a new element. When an alpha particle is emitted in a radioactive change, the product occupies a position with atomic number less by 2 than that of its parent in the chemical periodic table as a result of the decrease of 2 units of charge of the nucleus; the emission of a beta particle results in a shift of one place to the right, as a result of increase of 1 unit of charge on the nucleus. The loss of an alpha particle also means a decrease of 4 units of mass number; the ejection of a beta particle leaves the mass virtually unchanged. On the basis of this generalization, it is possible to represent the changes of atomic number and mass number occurring in three natural series or families of radioactive disintegration in the manner shown in Fig. III.1-1. The change due to emission of an alpha particle is represented by an arrow sloping downward and to the left; a beta-ray transformation is represented by a horizontal arrow pointing to the right. All the elements in any one vertical column have the same atomic number and are therefore isotopes of that element.

III.2. ALPHA PARTICLES

Alpha particles (nuclei of helium-4), although the most powerful of the radiations with respect to ionizing power, are unable to penetrate a few sheets of paper or thin aluminum foil; yet they can travel through several centimeters of air. It is evident, therefore, that different materials permit the passage of alpha particles to different degrees. The ranges of alpha particles in these substances are quite sharply defined and are found to depend upon the initial energy.

The kinetic energy of an alpha particle is given by the equation

$$E = \tfrac{1}{2}mv^2$$

$$= \left[2.08 \times 10^{-18} \frac{\text{Mev}}{(\text{cm/sec})^2} \right] v^2 \qquad \text{(III.2-1)}$$

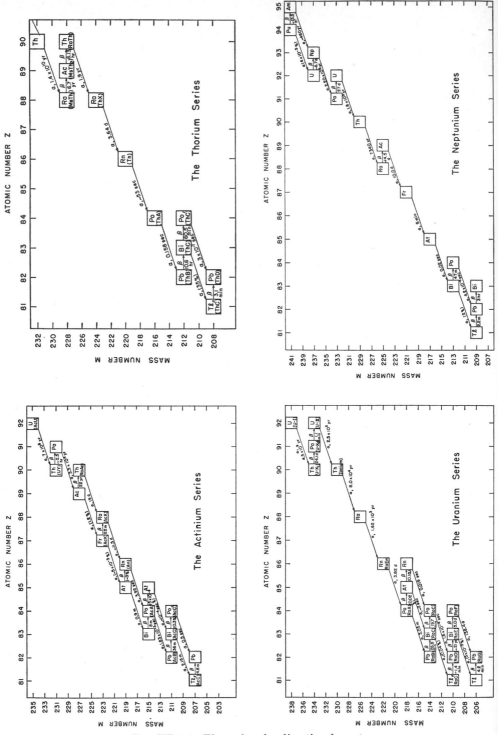

FIG. III.1-1. *The series of radioactive elements.*

if v is given in cm/sec. The direct measurement of the energies is made by determining the radii r of their circular paths in magnetic fields in instruments called *magnetic spectrographs*. Since by Equation I.2-2 speed is given by

$$v = (2e/m)Hr,$$

we find that

$$E = 2e^2H^2r^2/m. \tag{III.2-2}$$

Since the charge $2e$ and mass m are known, the evaluation of E requires only the determination of r in a field of known strength H (usually of the order of 10,000 gauss). The initial velocities of alpha particles from radioactive sources vary from about 1.4×10^9 to 2.2×10^9 cm/sec; the corresponding energies lie in the range between about 4 and 10 Mev.[1] The energies of alpha particles can also be determined from measurements of their absorption by matter or by their ranges.

It has been implicit thus far that all the alpha particles from a given source have virtually the same energy. This is not strictly the case. In some radioactive elements, such as thorium-C ($_{83}$Bi^{212}), alpha particles of different energies have been detected, giving rise to what is called an *alpha-particle spectrum*. The occurrence of such spectra can be accounted for, as we shall see later, by assuming the existence of definite energy levels in atomic nuclei.

Cloud-chamber photographs of an alpha-emitting source make it evident that the tracks exhibit a more or less characteristic length, known as the *range*, since these tracks terminate at practically the same distance from the source. In the main, the energy of the alpha particle is dissipated in "collisions" with electrons, resulting in the removal of the latter from the atom. Because of the great mass of the alpha particle compared with that of the electron, the path of the alpha particle is not deflected appreciably by these many encounters and is effectively linear.

The many collisions of the alpha particle in its passage through ordinary air may produce 50,000 to 100,000 ion pairs per centimeter by detaching electrons from the neutral molecules. The process of ionization requires the expenditure of about 32.5 ev by the alpha particle for each ion pair formed. (In the case of other gases, this energy loss may vary from about 20 ev to about 40 ev for each ion pair produced.) The energy lost and the ionization produced are not exactly propor-

[1] In highly accurate work, a relativity correction must be taken into account. The expressions employed are

$$v = (2e/m_0)Hr\left(1 - \frac{v^2}{c^2}\right)^{1/2}$$

and

$$T = m_0c^2\left\{\frac{1}{[1 - (v^2/c^2)]^{1/2}} - 1\right\},$$

where T is the relativistic kinetic energy.

tional. This is due to the fact that the ions produced possess varying amounts of kinetic energy, and that some electrons are merely lifted to metastable energy levels within the molecule, producing excited (but not ionized) atoms. As the alpha particle traverses its path, its energy and speed steadily diminish (see Fig. III.2-1). Thus toward the end of the path the energy and speed are greatly

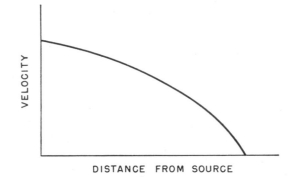

FIG. III.2-1. *Velocity of a typical alpha particle as a function of the distance from the source.*

reduced. In these circumstances there is a considerable probability that first one and then two electrons will adhere to the alpha particle, forming first He^+ and then the neutral helium atom, which has no ionizing power. Accordingly, the range of an alpha particle is defined as the distance it can travel through air under standard conditions from its source to the point at which it can no longer produce appreciable ionization. It is evident that the greater the initial energy of the alpha particle, the greater the number of collisions necessary to dissipate its energy and hence the longer the range. Experimentally it has been found that, to a fair approximation, the range R in centimeters is related to the initial speed v_0 in cm/sec by the equation

$$v_0{}^3 = 1.03 \times 10^{27} R, \tag{III.2-3}$$

a relation known as the Geiger formula. From Equations III.2-1 and III.2-3 it is seen that the initial energy E_0 of the alpha particle is given by

$$E_0 = 2.12 R^{2/3} \tag{III.2-4}$$

if E_0 is in Mev and R is in cm.

If a plot is made of the number of ion pairs produced in air by the alpha particle per unit length of path (the specific ionization of the alpha particle) at various distances from its source, as determined by suitable electrical detection instruments or by photographs, a curve such as that in Fig. III.2-2, called a *Bragg curve* in honor of W. H. Bragg, who first determined such curves systematically, is obtained. The shape of the curve is quite characteristic of alpha particles. As the distance from the source increases, the specific ionization of the alpha particle increases, at first slowly, then more rapidly, reaches a maximum, and then drops sharply almost to zero. The distance corresponding to the point R in Fig. III.2-2 represents the "extrapolated range" of the alpha particle from the

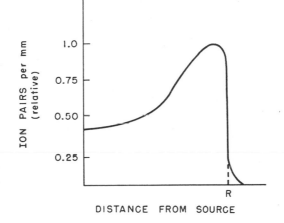

FIG. III.2-2. *Schematic representation of the average specific ionization of an alpha particle as a function of the distance from the source (the Bragg curve).*

given radioelement, as distinguished from the actual point of zero ion-pair production.

It is not difficult to account, in a general way, for the shape of the Bragg curve, for the specific ionization is found to be a function of the velocity. In general, the slower the velocity the greater is the specific ionization. For energies in excess of 1 Mev (velocities greater than 7×10^8 cm/sec) the specific ionization is approximately proportional to $1/v$, the reciprocal of the velocity. As the speed of the alpha particle decreases, it spends more time in the vicinity of each of the atoms and molecules of the medium which it encounters in its path. As a result, there is an increasing probability of removing an electron from an atom or molecule, thereby forming an ion pair. The specific ionization thus increases steadily at first, as the alpha particle recedes from the source. When ultimately the alpha particle is neutralized so as to form a helium atom, there no longer exists an ability to ionize the air, and the specific ionization ceases abruptly. The maximum specific ionization is reached by an alpha particle when it has a velocity of about 4.2×10^8 cm/sec (or an energy of about 370 kev).

The reason for the tail portion of the curve at the right in Fig. III.2-2 is that the alpha particles do not all lose exactly the same amount of energy in their encounters with the molecules in their paths. There is thus a statistical distribution of their energy losses in collisions. Hence they are not all transformed into neutral helium at precisely the same distance from the source. This slight variation in the range, frequently referred to as *straggling*, is also partly due to partial neutralization with the formation of He^+. The latter ions still possess ionizing power; hence they cause a slight extension of the range before they take up a second electron. Also, the capture of any one electron need not be permanent: the same alpha particle may capture and lose electrons many times before it eventually captures two electrons and ceases to cause ionization.

The range of an alpha particle also depends on the medium which it is traversing. A rough estimate of the range in an absorber is given by

$$R = 3.2 \times 10^{-4} R_0 A^{1/2}/d, \tag{III.2-5}$$

where R_0 is the range in air, d the density of the absorber, and A the average atomic weight. If the range in centimeters in a given medium is multiplied by the density in grams per cubic centimeter, the result is grams per square centimeter, which is equivalent to the thickness of material required to stop or absorb the alpha particles. Since this equivalent thickness (in mass per unit area) of the absorber is very small for solid absorbers, the result is often expressed in milligrams per square centimeter, obtained by multiplying by 1000. Thus

Equivalent thickness (in mg/cm²) = range (in cm) × density (in gm/cc) × 1000.
$$\tag{III.2-6}$$

III.3. BETA PARTICLES

The penetrating power of beta rays (electrons emitted in the radioactive decay of a nucleus) is approximately 100 times that of alpha rays. While the most energetic alpha particles may be completely absorbed in a few centimeters of air, beta particles may describe paths in air which are several hundred centimeters in length, or they may traverse a few millimeters of a solid such as aluminum. The ranges of beta rays through matter may have a considerable spread, unlike alpha particles, because they are so easily scattered by the atoms through which they pass. Because of the small mass of a beta particle as compared with that of a nucleus, elastic scattering may result in a large angle of deflection in a single collision. Thus the tracks of beta particles are not straight lines like those of alpha particles. At high energies the ranges of beta particles vary almost linearly with the energy. At low energies the range is more nearly proportional to the square of the energy.

The adsorption curve for beta rays displays a characteristic exponential shape, quite unlike the definite ranges exhibited by alpha particles. If a plot is made of the logarithm of the number of electrons passing through an absorber as a fraction of the thickness of the absorber, an approximately straight line is often obtained over a considerable region (see Fig. III.3-1). It will be noted that beyond a certain thickness of absorber the number of beta particles no longer decreases, but remains almost constant. This "tail" is due to the presence of bremsstrahlung (see below). If gamma radiation accompanies the beta radiation, the number of electrons in the tail is considerably higher.

For the light elements at least, the thickness (expressed in gm/cm²) of the material required to absorb or completely stop the beta particles is almost

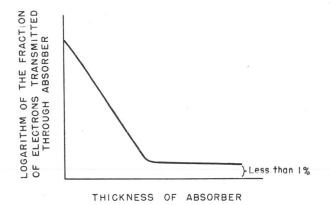

FIG. III.3-1. *Absorption curve for beta rays.*

completely independent of the nature of the absorber. This can be accounted for in the following manner. In their passage through matter, as we have seen, the beta particles are acted upon and deflected from a linear path by the attractions of the positively charged nuclei and the repulsions of the negatively charged electrons. As a beta particle approaches an atom, the attractive force of the nucleus is screened to some extent by the surrounding electrons of the atom. In addition, the approaching beta particle meets these repelling electrons first. Thus the greatest effect on a beta particle in altering its linear motion, as well as in slowing it, will be due to these electrons, presumably by inelastic collisions.

Consider the number of electrons in a gram of material. If N denotes the number of atoms in a gram of an element of atomic number Z, then the number of electrons in that gram is given by NZ. If N_0 denotes Avogadro's number and A the atomic weight,

$$NZ = N_0 Z/A. \qquad (III.3\text{-}1)$$

For elements of low atomic weight, it may be recalled that the number of protons in the nucleus (Z) is approximately equal to the number of neutrons ($A - Z$). (It is only for the heavier elements that the number of neutrons begins to exceed appreciably the number of protons.) Accordingly, for such materials

$$A \cong 2Z. \qquad (III.3\text{-}2)$$

By introducing Equation III.3-2 into the right-hand side of equation III.3-1, it is seen that the number of electrons in a gram of material is $\sim\frac{1}{2}N_0$, a constant independent of the nature of the material. If the stopping power of matter for beta rays is primarily dependent upon the actions of the electrons, then the stopping power on the basis of surface density (that is, the thickness in gm/cm²) will be independent of the kind of material employed.

The ionizing power of beta particles is appreciably less than that of alpha particles. This is why the tracks of beta particles in cloud-chamber photographs are much less distinct than those for alpha particles. The number of ion pairs produced per centimeter of path increases as the velocity of the particle decreases. Thus the specific ionization varies from about 25 ion pairs per centimeter at energies of about 2 Mev to about 200 per centimeter at 40 kev. The primary ions produced also have sufficient energy to cause further ionization, and the total number of ion pairs produced is 3 to 4 times that produced directly by the beta ray. As with alpha particles, too, the average energy loss per pair of primary ions formed in air is about 32.5 ev.

The velocities of beta rays may approach very closely to that of light. The masses of the electrons composing both high-speed cathode rays and beta rays are found to be represented quite exactly by the relativistic formula

$$m = m_0/[1 - (v^2/c^2)]^{1/2}, \tag{III.3-3}$$

in which m is the mass of the electron at the speed v, and m_0, the *rest mass*, is the mass at very low speeds. It may be shown that the kinetic energy of the electrons at any speed is given by the expression

$$\text{Kinetic energy} = (m - m_0)c^2. \tag{III.3-4}$$

The beta rays have the unique property, quite distinct from that of alpha particles or gamma rays, of having a continuous spectrum of energies. In each beta-ray spectrum there are electrons of all energies from almost zero up to a definite maximum value characteristic of the particular radionuclide. If the

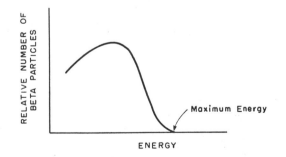

Fig. III.3-2. *General form of the distribution of energies among beta particles.*

relative number of betas possessing a particular energy is plotted against the energy, the points fall on a curve such as that depicted in Fig. III.3-2. The average energy of the beta particles is approximately 0.3 of the maximum energy.

Every beta ray is a potential producer of X rays. Just as in an X-ray tube, where the electrons striking the target give rise to the characteristic X rays of the target element superimposed on a continuous band of frequencies, so beta particles produce both kinds of X rays. The predominant X radiation is usually the continuous spectrum produced in inelastic collisions between the beta rays and the atoms of an absorber. These continuous X rays do not result from electronic transitions within the atom, but are due to the slowing down of the high-speed electrons. In accordance with Maxwell's electromagnetic theory, the deceleration of a moving charge must be accompanied by the emission of radiation.[1] Such radiation is frequently referred to as *bremsstrahlung*. As a general rule, the fraction of the kinetic energy of the electron converted into radiation in this manner increases with the energy of the electron and with the atomic number of the material in which it is slowed down. In tungsten, for example, a 10-Mev electron may lose about 50 per cent of its energy by radiation, whereas a 100-Mev electron may lose 90 per cent of its energy in this manner.

III.4. GAMMA RAYS

The gamma rays constitute that portion of the radiations from radioactive substances which is not deflected by electric and magnetic fields. They are not charged particles, but have the same kind of wave nature that is associated with X rays and visible light. This was proved in 1914 by demonstrating the diffraction of gamma rays from a suitable crystal. Direct measurements of the wavelengths of gamma rays give values of the order of 10^{-10} cm, corresponding to those for very short X rays. Gamma rays are thus a form of electromagnetic radiation of high frequency. The actual wavelengths of gamma rays depend upon the particular radionuclide from which they originate.

The frequencies ν of gamma rays are so high that the behavior of these radiations is almost entirely understood by considering them, in accordance with the suggestion of Einstein, as quanta of energy E, called photons, such that

$$E = h\nu$$
$$= hc/\lambda,$$

where h is Planck's constant, c the velocity of light, and λ the wavelength. Gamma rays interact strongly with matter, producing electrons, which makes detection relatively simple.

The energies of gamma rays extend from the X-ray region (about 100 kev) up to millions of electron volts. Just as optical and X-ray spectra arise from rearrangements of the orbital electrons in an atom, so the gamma rays arise from rearrangements of the particles in a nucleus after some form of excitation. The

---

[1]It will be recalled that the possibility of this phenomenon was rejected by Bohr when the electron was *bound* in the atom.

ejection of alpha and beta particles, for example, generally leaves the daughter nucleus in an excited state. The rearrangement of the nucleons takes place in about 10^{-12} second, and the liberated energy appears, as soon as the rearrangement occurs, in the form of gamma radiation.

In nonabsorbing collisions with matter a photon behaves as if it has a mass equal to $h\nu/c^2$ and thus a momentum of $h\nu/c$. When a photon of frequency ν is incident upon a free or loosely bound electron, the electron undergoes a recoil and a new photon of lesser frequency ν', and thus of lower energy, appears (see Fig. III.4-1). The collision between photon and electron is closely analogous to that

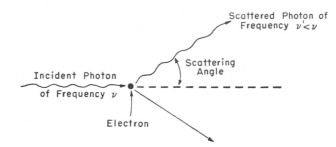

FIG. III.4-1. *Compton scattering.*

between two billiard balls of unequal mass, with the laws of conservation of energy and of momentum applying. The incident photon is never completely absorbed in this kind of process. The actual loss of energy is a function of the angle through which the photon is scattered, that is, of the angle between the directions of the photon before and after collision. This phenomenon, known as the *Compton effect* or as *Compton scattering* (the electrons are known as Compton recoils), is the most common method of interaction between gamma rays and matter. The electron acquires enough energy to cause ionization and is thus detected. The maximum energy of the electrons is a measure of the energy of the gamma-ray quanta. As a result of a series of such encounters in passing through matter, the energy of a gamma ray may be so greatly diminished that it is no longer detectable.

The second method of interaction is the *photoelectric effect*, in which an orbital electron is detached completely from an atom, with the simultaneous disappear-

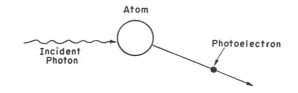

FIG. III.4-2. *Schematic representation of the photoelectric process.*

ance of the gamma photon which strikes it (see Fig. III.4-2). The electron acquires a kinetic energy equal to the original quantum energy less the energy of binding of the electron to the atom (the ionization potential of that electron, a small correction since the binding energy is never more than 100 kev and gamma rays are usually very energetic). Hence the kinetic energy of the electron is not much less than that of the photon. Again, it is the ionization produced by the photoelectron which renders the detection of the gamma ray possible.

A third method of interaction is that of *pair production* (not to be confused with the formation of ion pairs), in which an energetic gamma photon disappears, to be replaced by an electron and a positron (see Fig. III.4-3), at the cost of the energy supplied by the gamma ray. Pair production cannot occur unless the

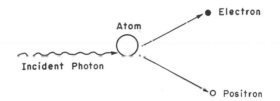

FIG. III.4-3. *Schematic representation of pair production.*

radiation has an energy exceeding 1.02 Mev, since this is the minimum energy required by the mass-energy relation to account for the total mass of the pair. Further, this process of annihilation of the gamma quantum can occur only in the presence of matter, for it is otherwise impossible to conserve both energy and momentum. Any energy of the photon in excess of 1.02 Mev appears as kinetic energies of the particles.

In some cases, particularly with elements of high atomic number, it is possible that a gamma photon, upon emerging from a nucleus, may produce a kind of photoelectric effect with one of the orbital electrons of the same atom. In doing so, the whole of the gamma-ray energy is transferred to the electron, which is then ejected from the atom with a kinetic energy equal to the energy of the gamma quantum less the binding energy of the electron in the atom. This is called *internal conversion*. The effect of internal conversion is to inject sharp lines onto the continuous beta-ray spectrum. Since internal conversion leaves a vacancy in one of the inner electron shells, the emission of conversion electrons is always accompanied by the emission of characteristic X rays of the daughter (not the parent) element.

Gamma radiation is very penetrating and is not completely stopped by matter. Instead, its intensity decreases in accordance with an exponential law; thus there is no definite maximum range as with alpha and beta particles. All three of the processes described above contribute to the absorption of gamma radiation. (Two other processes, elastic scattering and photonuclear disintegration, also occur, but their contributions are generally small, at least below 10-Mev radiation.) The photoelectric effect and the process of pair formation depend markedly on the element used as the absorber; however, the Compton effect is independent of the material, depending only on the number of electrons present and on the energy of the gamma ray. The photoelectric effect is of greatest importance for the heavy elements and for relatively low-energy gamma radiation, since it is apparent that the more tightly bound the electron the greater is its ability to reduce the intensity of the gamma radiation. The formation of the electron-positron pair is greater in the proximity of heavy elements and also for energetic radiation; the effect increases rapidly as the energy of the gamma-ray photon exceeds 1.02 Mev. The importance of the Compton effect decreases smoothly with increasing energy (approximately as $1/E$). It is particularly important in the elements of low atomic weight and for gamma rays with energies that are not too high nor too low.

III.5. POSITRONS

In spite of the absence of experimental evidence for the existence of a positive electron, i.e., a particle equal in mass to the electron but carrying a positive charge, in 1930, P. A. M. Dirac, the English physicist, postulated and predicted, on the basis of some theoretical arguments, that such a particle was possible. Proof of the existence of the positive electron, or positron as it is more often called, was obtained in 1932 (also the year in which the neutron was discovered) at the California Institute of Technology by C. D. Anderson from cloud-chamber photographs taken in conjunction with studies of cosmic rays.

The creation of the positron in Anderson's photograph has been attributed to pair production by a high-energy gamma. Since then, positrons have been found to be produced from the disintegration of certain artificially prepared radioactive nuclei. Since positrons were rare enough to elude discovery for many years, it would seem that they are not a universal constituent of matter as are electrons.

A positron was the first elementary particle discovered to have only a transient existence. The average life varies with its environment, usually being of the order of 10^{-9} second in solids and liquids, and of the order of 10^{-7} second in gases at normal pressures. It appears that when a positron and an electron collide, the charges neutralize one another and the particles are mutually annihilated (the inverse process to that of pair production), leaving only energy in the form of radiation, often called *annihilation radiation*, similar to gamma rays.[1] It is for this reason that the positron had proved so difficult to detect. As might be expected from Einstein's mass-energy relationship, the energy of the radiation is

[1]It has been shown experimentally, at least in the case of gases under low pressure, that prior to annihilation, a positron can capture an electron (or be captured) to form a system, called positronium, analogous to a hydrogen atom. Positronium has a mean lifetime of the order of 10^{-10} second.

1.02 Mev, a contribution of 0.51 Mev from the mass of each particle. If this energy were to be liberated as one quantum, it would be anticipated that the frequency would be 4.13×10^{21} per second, corresponding to a wavelength of 0.0121 Å. However, it is observed that the wavelength of the annihilation radiation is 0.0242 Å, corresponding to 0.51 Mev. This indicates that two quanta are emitted, proceeding in opposite directions in order to conserve momentum as required by the laws of mechanics.

III.6. THE NEUTRON

Since the neutron carries no electric charge, it produces no appreciable ionization in its path, so that it cannot be observed directly. Also as a consequence of its neutrality, the neutron will traverse thick layers of heavy elements with little loss in energy. It undergoes a force only when it comes within extremely close range of a nucleus. The interaction with the nucleus may be regarded as a collision, which may be elastic or inelastic.

Neutrons are detected and counted by utilizing secondary ionizing particles produced in collisions with nuclei. The most common method makes use of the fact that the boron-10 isotope easily captures a slow neutron and then emits an alpha particle. By utilizing a boron compound in a counter tube of proper design, the secondary ionization by the alpha particle permits the neutrons to be counted without difficulty. Another type of neutron detector and counter makes use of the ability of the neutron to cause fission. Still other kinds of detectors have been devised.

Like the positron, the neutron does not have a permanent existence. If not captured by some nucleus, a free neutron undergoes beta decay with a half-life of about 13 minutes, being transformed into a proton. It must not be assumed, however, that a neutron is a close combination of a proton and an electron. In fact, a proton in certain nuclei can turn into a neutron by losing its positive charge.

III.7. THE NEUTRINO

Experimental evidence indicates that beta decay is essentially a process in which one neutron in the nucleus is transformed into a proton. The problem of the continuous distribution of energy among the beta particles thus formed (see § III.3) was a matter of concern to nuclear physicists for a long time. It seemed highly improbable that it could be due to the existence of a continuous series of energy levels in either parent or daughter elements, since all other evidence pointed to the presence of definite discrete energies. If the variation in energy among the beta particles was due to transitions between different states of nuclear energy, then there should be a continuous distribution of gamma-ray energies to correspond to that of the beta particles; but no such phenomenon has been observed. The emission of a beta particle, like the emission of an alpha particle, must be accompanied by a definite change of energy; there is reason for believing that this is the maximum energy $E_{\max}$ observed for beta particles.

There then arises the problem of accounting for the additional energy in the case of the great majority of beta particles whose energy is less than $E_{\max}$. Furthermore, measurements of the linear momenta of a beta particle and the recoil atom from which it was ejected seemed to violate the law of conservation of momentum. So as not to violate any of the laws of conservation, Pauli in 1927 suggested that the emission of a beta particle was accompanied by the emission of a *neutrino*. This was assumed to be an electrically neutral particle (required by conservation of electric charge) of rest mass very much less than that of an electron. The creation of the beta particle in the nucleus composed of protons and neutrons would then be represented by the process

$$_0n^1 \rightarrow {}_1p^1 + {}_{-1}e^0 + {}_0\nu^0 + E_{\max},$$

where $_0\nu^0$ symbolizes a neutrino. Pauli suggested that the total available energy, $E_{\max}$, was divided between the electron and the neutrino. If the electron takes all the energy and the neutrino none, the measured energy of the electron would be $E_{\max}$. If the neutrino takes all the energy, the electron would not even be detectable. Neither of these extreme processes would be very likely, so that for the most part the energy is split between the two.

In view of its very small rest mass, certainly not more than $\frac{1}{2000}$ of the mass of an electron, and the absence of an electric charge, the neutrino would be expected to pass readily through matter and hence would be difficult to detect. It has been estimated that a neutrino would have to travel about 300,000 miles in the air, on the average, before it would strike a nucleus. A further estimate gives the minute extent of ionization produced by the neutrino as 10^{-17} ion pair per centimeter of path. Nonetheless, the neutrino has been detected experimentally by a group of scientists at Los Alamos.

Since it is not believed that nuclei contain positrons, it has been supposed that a positron is created in the nucleus by a process analogous to that for beta emission:

$$_1H^1 \rightarrow {}_0n^1 + {}_1e^0 + {}_0\bar{\nu}^0 + E_{\max},$$

where $_0\bar{\nu}^0$ is the symbol for an *antineutrino*, the latter being postulated to account for the energy distribution among the positrons.

III.8. MESONS

In the years since 1935 a whole set of new subatomic particles of "medium" mass (about 200 to 300 times the mass of an electron) has been discovered in cosmic rays as well as produced artificially by high-energy accelerators. The first evidence for their existence was obtained when it was shown that there were charged particles which could traverse thick lead plates without apparently being deflected from their straight path or producing a cascade or any other kind of additional track. The particles later proved to be lighter than protons but much heavier than electrons. Some carried a positive and some a negative charge. As a class they are known as mesons, a name chosen to indicate that the mass is intermediate between those of the electron and the proton.

The π-meson, or pion, may occur with a positive, a negative, or no charge. The charged pion has a mass 276 times that of an electron, whereas the mass of the neutral meson is 265 times that of an electron. The μ-meson or muon (which was the first kind of meson to be discovered) is somewhat lighter, about 210 electronic masses, and may have a positive or negative charge. Neutral muons are not known. Because they are heavier than electrons, mesons produce a higher specific ionization in their tracks and, on the whole, are more penetrating.

Mesons have a very ephemeral existence. The positive π-mesons have been found to decay, forming positive μ-mesons. The mean life has been estimated as 2×10^{-8} second. The decay of the π-meson has been supposed to be accompanied by the emission of a neutrino:

$$\pi \rightarrow \mu + \nu + \text{energy.}$$

Some negative π-mesons decay similarly, also with a mean life of about 10^{-8} second; but by far the larger proportion are captured by nuclei to which they are strongly attracted. This capture results in the complete disintegration or explosion of the nucleus. From the kind of photographs obtained, these explosions are known as "stars." The neutral pion decays into two photons in something like 10^{-15} second.

Positively charged muons spontaneously decay into a positron and two neutrinos. The negatively charged μ-meson decays into a fast electron, a neutrino, and an antineutrino. The average life is about 10^{-6} second in each case.

A complex of particles, known as K-mesons, has been found with masses about 966 times that of an electron. They were first found in cosmic rays, but have since been produced in modern accelerators, although much more rarely than pions or muons.

$Hyperon$ is the name given to a group of particles with masses greater than that of the neutron or proton, ranging from about 2000 to 3000 times the mass of an electron. They probably contain nucleons as constituents. The one known as Λ° was the first to be found (in 1947). It was revealed in a cloud-chamber photograph as an apparently neutral particle, leaving no track, which spontaneously decayed in its flight, yielding two track-producing products. The charged hyperon $\Sigma^\pm$ appears to be a closely related particle. The particle Ξ^- is the heaviest hyperon discovered thus far; it decays in very short order into Λ° plus a negative pion. The Λ° in turn decays into a proton plus another negative pion with a release of about 35 Mev in energy. Both pions of course go through the usual decay, ending up as electrons and neutrinos.

III.9. THE ANTIPROTON AND THE ANTINEUTRON

Both the antiproton and antineutron have been discovered from the use of the Berkeley bevatron. The antiproton has a mass corresponding to that of the proton, but has a negative charge. The antineutron was recognized by its lack of deflection in a magnetic field and by the characteristic energy released upon annihilation. The annihilation of antineutrons and antiprotons gives a nuclear explosion, accompanied by emission of protons, neutrons, nuclear fragments, and many of the heavy mesons. The neutron and the antineutron presumably differ in the orientation of the magnetic moment relative to the spin vector.

The discovery of antimatter, whereby each elementary particle seems to have a counterpart of the same mass but of opposite electric charge, has presented a new and unresolved challenge to science. There has been much conjecture, for example in cosmological studies, whether or not there exist stars and galaxies composed of antiparticles. At present there is no reason to believe that nature should show a preference for either particles as we know them or antiparticles. If such galaxies do exist, there does seem to be evidence that each must be composed primarily of one or the other kind of material. Were this not so, particle-antiparticle annihilation would probably occur to a greater extent than has been observed.

III.10. RADIATION HAZARDS

All radiations from radioactive materials have deleterious biological effects. The harmful consequences result from the ionizing effects of the radiations, but little is known of the exact mechanism by which the damage is produced. It is known that the radiations affect the individual cells of the body. These may be killed outright by a sufficiently intense dose, or cell division may be delayed by exposure.

Because of their relatively small penetrating power, the dangers associated with external alpha-particle sources are not serious. Unfortunately, however, if alpha emitters are accidentally ingested or inhaled, some, such as radium or plutonium, tend to accumulate in certain portions of the body where the continued action can be harmful. Thus, if radium or plutonium is localized in growing bones, a region very sensitive to radiations, the radiation intensity within a few microns of the radioactive material is tremendous. The potency of plutonium is revealed by the observation that as little as 0.1 μg of plutonium-239 deposited in the bone is sufficient to cause carcinoma.

Beta particles are able to penetrate only a few millimeters of tissue. Thus the dangers from exposure to an external source are easily mitigated by light shielding. (It is not advisable to use shielding incorporating a heavy element, since this would tend to cause the production of bremsstrahlung.) The damage from ingestion of beta emitters also results from localization in particular parts of the body, which may give rise to highly damaging intensities.

Gamma rays and X rays offer a serious hazard since they can travel long distances through air and can penetrate quite deeply into the body. Thus precautions must be taken against exposure to external sources of these radiations. In general, the use of sufficiently thick shielding composed of lead or other dense substances is suitable for preventing exposure of the body.

Neutrons, too, can penetrate quite deeply into the body. Neutrons can react with several of the elements in the body, producing highly energetic gamma radiations. Recoil protons of large kinetic energies may also be formed, and these produce intense ionization along their paths. The type of shielding needed for neutrons depends on the proportions and the energies of fast neutrons present in the radiation. Neutron shielding is best accomplished by materials which contain hydrogen. Tanks of water containing a small amount of dissolved borax serve very well. Concrete containing as much water as possible serves as a compromise shielding material for both neutron and gamma rays.

Chapter IV

NATURAL RADIOACTIVITY

IV.1. THE LAW OF RADIOACTIVE DECAY

Even though the radioactivity of some materials, such as radium or uranium, appears to be permanent, actually all radioactivity becomes weaker with time. For some substances the rate of decay of activity is extremely rapid, whereas for others it is exceedingly slow.

Radioactivity seems to be a pure chance phenomenon and should be describable as a statistical process. The laws of probability should apply. The liberation of a particle from a given unstable nucleus is independent of the liberation of the same (or of different) particles from other nuclei (whether identical or different).

It is assumed that every nucleus of a radioactive species has some definite and characteristic probability of disintegration in a unit of time, independent of its past history and the present circumstances of the nucleus. The actual lifetime of any given nucleus is indeterminate until the moment at which decay occurs. The probability of decay per unit time is frequently denoted by λ. If the time over which the nucleus is observed is Δt, then the probability of decay should depend on the duration of the time interval, so that it becomes equal to $\lambda \Delta t$.

On the other hand, observation is made, not of a single nucleus, but rather of a large number of them, say N, so that statistical laws should apply. In the interval of time Δt we may observe that a number of them, ΔN, do disintegrate. The ratio $\Delta N/N$ then denotes the ratio of the number of cases of disintegration observed to the total possible number of decays, given by decay of all N nuclei, and so this ratio is then representative of the probability of any one nucleus disintegrating in the time Δt. Accordingly, equation of the two probabilities gives

$$\Delta N/N = -\lambda \Delta t$$

or

$$\frac{\Delta N}{\Delta t} = -\lambda N, \tag{IV.1-1}$$

the minus sign being employed since the number of nuclei is decreasing. In other words, the number of nuclei which have decayed on the average in the time Δt is proportional to the total number of nuclei present at the beginning of the time interval. Equation IV.1-1 gives the expression for the average rate of change of the potentially radioactive nuclei. By letting the time interval Δt get shorter and shorter, the instantaneous rate of change is obtained in the form of a differential equation:

$$\frac{dN}{dt} = \lim_{\Delta t \to 0} \frac{\Delta N}{\Delta t} = -\lambda N. \tag{IV.1-2}$$

This may be integrated to give

$$N = N_0 e^{-\lambda t}, \tag{IV.1-3}$$

where N_0 represents the number of atoms at time $t = 0$. The equivalent logarithmic forms

$$\ln(N/N_0) = -\lambda t \tag{IV.1-4}$$

and

$$\log(N/N_0) = -0.4343\,\lambda t \tag{IV.1-5}$$

may be used. These equations indicate that the number of atoms out of an original total N_0 which have not experienced disintegration decreases exponentially with time. The exponential law (IV.1-3) was first formulated by Rutherford and Soddy in 1902.

The disintegration law applies universally to all radioactive nuclei. It is only the constant λ, frequently called the *decay constant* or the *radioactive constant*, that is different for each species; no two have exactly the same decay constant. As stated above, λ denotes the probability of the decay of a nucleus of the particular radioactive species in unit time. Its value depends only upon the nature of the species. The values of λ for the known naturally radioactive nuclei vary between 3×10^6 sec^{-1} for Th-C′ (Po^{212}) and 1.58×10^{-18} sec^{-1} for thorium-232, a range of over 10^{24}.

Upon rearrangement, Equation IV.1-5 may be written as

$$\log N = \log N_0 - 0.4343\,\lambda t. \tag{IV.1-6}$$

If, then, a plot[1] is made of $\log N$ against time t, a straight line should be obtained. The slope of this line will be equal to -0.4343λ. Hence such a plot can be used to determine the value of λ for a given radioelement, one of the most significant measurements that can be made with a radioactive species.

Equations IV.1-1 through IV.1-6 refer to the number of atoms of the parent element present, which often is difficult or impossible to measure. It is far easier to observe the effects of the radiations emitted during the actual change. This would mean an observation of an effect proportional to the *rate of decay*. In other words, we measure the *activity A* (that is, the total number of disintegrations per unit time) of the sample as a function of time.[2] The activity of the species will be

---

[1]This is most easily done on semilogarithmic graph paper.
[2]The activity A might be the counting rate of a Geiger counter or the discharge rate of an electroscope, or some such quantity.

proportional to the number of radioactive nuclei N present at the time and to the probability that a nucleus will decay in unit time:

$$A = k\lambda N, \qquad (IV.1\text{-}7)$$

k being a constant of proportionality.[3] In other words, we expect twice as many disintegrations per unit time in a sample containing twice as many atoms, and so forth. From Equations IV.1-2 and IV.1-7 there is obtained

$$\frac{dA}{dt} = -\lambda A, \qquad (IV.1\text{-}8)$$

which may be integrated to give

$$A = A_0 e^{-\lambda t}; \qquad (IV.1\text{-}9)$$

$$\ln A = \ln A_0 - \lambda t; \qquad (IV.1\text{-}10)$$

$$\log A = \log A_0 - 0.4343\,\lambda t, \qquad (IV.1\text{-}11)$$

where $A_0\ (= \lambda k N_0)$ is the initial activity of the sample. The usual procedure is to plot $\log A$ against t, with λ being determined by the slope of the straight line obtained (see Fig. IV.1-1).

IV.2. THE HALF-LIFE

A convenient criterion for comparing the rates of radioactive decay of different species is through a specification of the characteristic *half-life*, symbolized by T, of each radioactive nuclide. The half-life is defined as the time required for the number of radioactive nuclei or for their activity to decay to one-half of the initial value. It represents the time interval in which the *chance* of survival of a particular radioactive atom is exactly 50 per cent. A very active species will have a short half-life, while a feebly radioactive substance will have a long half-life. It is possible, of course, to choose a one-third-life or any other fractional life, but traditionally the half-life is chosen for the comparison.

FIG. IV.1-1. *Graphical determination of constants associated with radioactivity.*

By definition, then, after the lapse of a half-time $t = T$ from some initial time $t = 0$, the number N of radioactive atoms of the species considered will be one-half of the initial number N_0:

$$N = N_0/2. \qquad (IV.2\text{-}1)$$

[3]The constant k, which may be called the detection coefficient, will depend on the nature of the instrument used, the efficiency, the geometrical arrangement, etc.

Upon using this equation in Equation IV.1-5 and replacing t by T (for it is only at this time that Equation IV.2-1 is valid) it is seen that

$$\log \tfrac{1}{2} = -0.4343 \, \lambda T, \qquad \text{(IV.2-2)}$$

so that

$$\log 2 - 0.4343 \, \lambda T. \qquad \text{(IV.2-3)}$$

Thus

$$T = 0.6931/\lambda \qquad \text{(IV.2-4)}$$

$$= (\ln 2)/\lambda,$$

so that the half-life is inversely proportional to the decay constant. If λ is known, the half-life of the radioelement can be calculated very simply, and vice versa. The half-lives of the known radioactive species range from a few microseconds for the most unstable to billions of years for those which are only slightly unstable.

To obtain the half-life it is not necessary to calculate the decay constant first. By using a logarithmic plot such as in Fig. IV.1-1, it is only necessary to read off the time required for the activity to fall by a factor of $\log 2 = 0.301$. It is immaterial where the initial time is chosen; at any given time there will always be some initial number N_0 of atoms which have not disintegrated, and at a time T thereafter one-half of these will be gone. No matter how many atoms have decayed, the decay constant and the half-life are the same for the remainder.

An examination of the experimental values of the half-lives and energies of particles emitted in radioactive decay shows that it is approximately true that, as the half-life decreases, the energy increases. Thus Geiger and Nuttall in 1911 found that the logarithm of the energy (or range) of an alpha particle was a linear function of the logarithm of the half-life for each of the three naturally occurring radioactive families. The Geiger-Nuttall rule has been of great value in estimating the half-lives (and thus the decay constants) of very long-lived or very short-lived elements from measurements of the ranges of the emitted alpha particles. A similar relationship holds for several groups of naturally occurring beta emitters (the Sargent rule).

The fact that radioactive elements disintegrate in accordance with an exponential law has some important consequences. Suppose, for the sake of illustration, that a particular radioelement has a half-life of 1 hour ($T = 1$ hour). Starting, say, with 1 gm of the element, at the end of 1 hour, one-half (0.5 gm) will remain. During the next hour, one-half of this amount (0.25 gm) will disintegrate, leaving 0.25 gm. By the end of the third hour, another 0.125 gm will have decayed, and so on. In each successive hour the actual amount which disintegrates is less than in the preceding hour, although it is the same fraction of the amount present at the beginning of the particular hour (see Fig. IV.2-1). In general, since the activity is reduced to one-half of its initial value in the time T, the fraction remaining

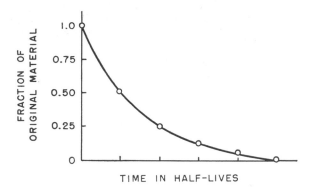

F$_{\text{IG}}$. IV.2-1. *The meaning of half-life as applied to radioactive decay.*

after n such intervals (a total time interval of nT) will be $(\frac{1}{2})^n$. Although this fraction can become very small, theoretically it can never fall to zero. However, after ten half-lives the activity has fallen to

$$(\tfrac{1}{2})^{10} \cong 0.001$$

times the original activity so that the remaining activity may be considered small in comparison with the original value.

The *curie*, named in honor of the discoverers of radium and originally devised to express the activity of a gram of radium, is defined as the quantity of any radioactive species decaying at a rate of 3.70×10^{10} disintegrations per second.[1] The rate of decay is given by the product λN, or, making use of Equation IV.2-4, by

$$\begin{array}{cc} \text{Rate of decay} \\ \text{(disintegrations/second)} \end{array} = \frac{0.693N}{T}, \qquad (\text{IV.2-5})$$

if T is given in seconds. Now a sample of a radioisotope with a mass of g grams contains

$$N = (6.02 \times 10^{23})g/A \qquad (\text{IV.2-6})$$

atoms, where 6.02×10^{23} atoms/gram-atom is the Avogadro number and A the isotopic weight. Upon combining these equations and introducing the definition of the curie, it follows that

$$\text{Number of curies} = 1.13 \times 10^{13}\, g/AT \qquad (\text{IV.2-7})$$

or that the mass of a substance having an activity of one curie is given by

$$\text{Mass per curie (grams)} = AT/1.13 \times 10^{13}. \qquad (\text{IV.2-8})$$

[1]For historical reasons mainly there has been some confusion about the use of the curie as a standard unit of radioactivity. A proposal has been made to use the *rutherford* (symbolized rd), defined as the amount of a radioactive substance which gives 10^6 disintegrations per second, as a standard.

For a substance with a short half-life very little material is needed to provide a curie of activity. In the case of a radionuclide with a very long half-life, a large amount may be required.

IV.3. THE AVERAGE OR MEAN LIFE

The actual life of any particular atom of a radioactive species can have any value from zero to infinity. It is not possible to tell when a particular nucleus will disintegrate. Like the half-life, however, the *average life* of a large number of radioactive atoms is a definite and important quantity. As the name implies, the value is obtained simply by adding the total times of life of each of the N_0 atoms of a radioactive sample and then dividing by N_0:

$$\text{Mean life} = \frac{\text{life of atom 1} + \text{life of atom 2} + \cdots + \text{life of atom } N_0}{N_0} \qquad \text{(IV.3-1)}$$

$$= (\text{total life of all atoms})/N_0.$$

In any particular case, of course, it is not possible to observe the disintegration of a single nucleus. Rather, the number of disintegrations is observed over a comparatively small time interval Δt at some time t. Suppose, then, that it is observed that a number ΔN_1 of the atoms disintegrate during the interval Δt_1 at the time t_1 measured from an arbitrary zero of time, t_0. Then the quantity $(\Delta N_1)t_1$ will be the total lifetime after t_0 of all the nuclei which disintegrated between times t_1 and $t_1 + \Delta t_1$. Similarly, $(\Delta N_2)t_2$ will be the total lifetime after t_0 of the ΔN_2 atoms which decayed between times t_2 and $t_2 + \Delta t_2$. Proceeding in this manner, it is found that the total lifetime after t_0 of all N_0 atoms is given by

$$(\Delta N_1)t_1 + (\Delta N_2)t_2 + \cdots = \sum_{t_i=0}^{\infty} t_i(\Delta N_i). \qquad \text{(IV.3-2)}$$

This is the numerator on the right-hand side of Equation IV.3-1, so that

$$\text{Mean life} = \frac{1}{N_0} \sum_{t_i=0}^{\infty} t_i(\Delta N_i). \qquad \text{(IV.3-3)}$$

By allowing the time interval Δt_i to approach zero, the sum becomes an integral, so that there is obtained

$$\text{Mean life } t_m = \frac{1}{N_0} \int_{t=0}^{t=\infty} t\,dN. \qquad \text{(IV.3-4)}$$

From Equation IV.1-2

$$dN = -\lambda N\,dt, \qquad \text{(IV.3-5)}$$

so that Equation IV.3-4 becomes

$$t_m = \frac{\lambda}{N_0} \int_{t=0}^{t=\infty} N t\,dt. \qquad \text{(IV.3-6)}$$

With the use of Equation IV.1-3, in order to express N as a function of time so that the integration may be performed, there is obtained

$$t_m = \frac{\lambda N_0}{N_0} \int_{t=0}^{t=\infty} te^{-\lambda t}dt \qquad \text{(IV.3-7)}$$
$$= 1/\lambda.$$

Alternatively, by using Equation IV.2-4, the mean life may be expressed in terms of the half-life:

$$t_m = 1.44T. \qquad \text{(IV.3-8)}$$

If t_m is substituted for t in Equation IV.1-5, we see, since by equation IV.3-7 $\lambda t_m = 1$, that the mean life is the time required for the number of atoms, or for their activity, to fall to $e^{-1} = 0.368$ of any initial value.

IV.4. MIXTURES OF UNRELATED RADIOELEMENTS

Very often several unrelated radioactive isotopes are present in the same sample. In such a case the total activity A is obtained as the sum of the individual activities:

$$A = c_1A_1 + c_2A_2 + c_3A_3 + \cdots. \qquad \text{(IV.4-1)}$$

Again, the coefficients c_1, c_2, c_3, ... are factors essentially incorporating the efficiency of detection of each type of radiation.

As an example, the logarithm of the total activity of a mixture of two radioactive isotopes of appreciably different half-lives is plotted against time in Fig.

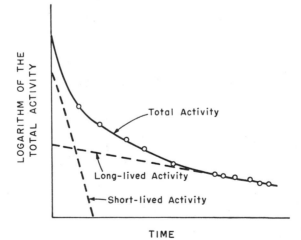

FIG. IV.4-1. *Radioactive decay in a sample having two components of appreciably different half-lives.*

IV.4-1. The line is no longer straight, but curved. After a sufficient length of time, however, the activity of the shorter-lived component will be negligible in comparison with that of the longer-lived constituent. Thus at the right-hand side of Fig. IV.4-1 the activity is essentially due to the latter. Accordingly, the decay constant or the half-life of the long-lived isotope is readily determined from the right-hand portion of the curve. The half-life of the other component may then be estimated by subtracting the contribution of the longer-lived constituent through extrapolation back to zero time of the linear portion of the total activity, for the resulting plot will represent the decay curve of the shorter-lived activity. (This procedure can be applied to cases where there are more than two components if the half-lives are sufficiently different.)

IV.5. RADIOACTIVE EQUILIBRIUM

The change of the amount of radioactive substance may be quite complicated if a radioactive isotope is itself a product of radioactive decay, or more particularly, if the radioactive substance is a member of a long radioactive chain. This is the common situation in dealing with the naturally occurring radioactive elements. The change in the number N_1 of atoms of the first member of a radioactive series obeys the simple differential decay law:

$$dN_1 = -\lambda_1 N_1 dt, \qquad (IV.5\text{-}1)$$

where λ_1 is the decay constant of this first member. However, the change in the number N_2 of the atoms of the second member of the series is

$$dN_2 = \lambda_1 N_1 dt - \lambda_2 N_2 dt. \qquad (IV.5\text{-}2)$$

The first term on the right-hand side expresses the formation of N_2 resulting from the decay of the first member of the series; the second term represents the disintegration of the second kind of atom. Likewise, for the third member,

$$dN_3 = \lambda_2 N_2 dt - \lambda_3 N_3 dt. \qquad (IV.5\text{-}3)$$

Similar differential equations hold for further members of the series of disintegration.

In the simplest case of a radioactive chain, with but two species (parent and daughter) involved and ending with an inactive third isotope, the equations can be integrated to give

$$N_1 = N_{10} e^{-\lambda_1 t} \qquad (IV.5\text{-}4)$$

$$N_2 = \frac{\lambda_1}{\lambda_2 - \lambda_1} N_{10}(e^{-\lambda_1 t} - e^{-\lambda_2 t}) + N_{20} e^{-\lambda_2 t}. \qquad (IV.5\text{-}5)$$

In these equations N_{10} and N_{20} are, respectively, the initial numbers of atoms of kinds 1 and 2 at the arbitrarily chosen zero of time. The first group of terms in Equation IV.5-5 shows the growth of the daughter from the parent and the decay of these daughter atoms; the last term gives the contribution at any time from those daughter atoms which may have been present initially.

In practice there occur several important cases involving parent-daughter pairs of radioactive species. These depend on the ratio of the half-lives or decay constants of the substances involved. For example, if the parent is much longer-lived than the daughter ($\lambda_1 \ll \lambda_2$ or $T_1 \gg T_2$), a state of so-called *radioactive* or *secular equilibrium* is reached. After a certain time the ratio of the numbers of atoms (and thereby the ratio of the disintegration rates) of parent and daughter become constant. This can be readily seen from Equations IV.5-4 and IV.5-5. After t becomes sufficiently large, $e^{-\lambda_2 t}$ becomes negligible compared with $e^{-\lambda_1 t}$, and also $N_{20}e^{-\lambda_2 t}$ becomes negligible. Then Equation IV.5-5 may be written as

$$N_2 = \frac{\lambda_1}{\lambda_2 - \lambda_1} N_{10}e^{-\lambda_1 t}. \qquad \text{(IV.5-6)}$$

If this equation is combined with Equation IV.5-4 there results

$$\frac{N_1}{N_2} = \frac{\lambda_2 - \lambda_1}{\lambda_1} \simeq \frac{\lambda_2}{\lambda_1} = \frac{T_1}{T_2}. \qquad \text{(IV.5-7)}$$

Since λ_1 and λ_2 are constants, it follows that the ratio of the amounts of parent and daughter will be constant in this condition of radioactive equilibrium.

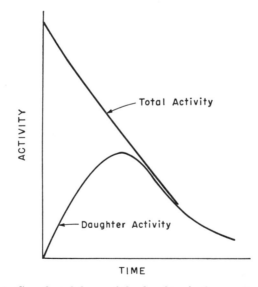

FIG. IV.5-1. *Growth and decay of the daughter in the case that the parent has a shorter half-life.*

Equation IV.5-7 has proved to be very useful in measuring long half-lives. If the ratio of the equilibrium amounts of the two elements can be determined, say by chemical analysis, and if the relatively short half-life of the daughter is known, the half-life of the parent can then be calculated. For example, uranium-238, an alpha emitter of very long half-life, decays into uranium X_1 (Th^{234}), which is a beta emitter with a half-life of 24.6 days. By analyzing uranium minerals in which secular equilibrium has been established, the half-life of uranium-238 is determined as 4.5×10^9 years.

If the parent is shorter-lived than the daughter ($\lambda_1 > \lambda_2$ or $T_1 < T_2$) no equilibrium is attained at any time. If the substance originally contains none of the daughter ($N_{2_0} = 0$), Equation IV.5-5 then shows that as the parent decays the amount of daughter will rise, pass through a maximum, and eventually decay with the characteristic half-life of the daughter, as in Figure IV.5-1.

Chapter V

THE NUCLEUS

V.1. NUCLEAR SPIN

It may be recalled (see § 1.6) that to explain certain observations the revised Bohr theory (and also quantum mechanics) required an assumption that the electron possessed a spin angular momentum of $\frac{1}{2}(h/2\pi)$. The number $\frac{1}{2}$ is called the spin quantum number or, simply, the spin of the electron. As in the case of electrons, in order to explain certain analogous observations it appears that nuclei also must possess an intrinsic angular momentum (that is, they undergo a rotation of some kind), called the *nuclear spin*. The nuclear spin is not observed directly but is measured indirectly in terms of the effects it produces. Several methods, some of them based on spectroscopic studies and others involving the behavior of atoms in a magnetic field, have been devised for such determinations. The experimental results indicate that the nuclear spin is either integral or half-integral, depending upon the specific nucleus.

In order to explain the values of the nuclear spins, the nuclear angular momentum may be thought of as a vector sum of the angular momenta associated with the individual constituent nucleons. It has become evident that, like electrons, individual protons and neutrons can have spin quantum numbers of $+\frac{1}{2}$ and $-\frac{1}{2}$ only. The spins of some light particles are given in Table V.1-1.

TABLE V.1-1

SPINS AND MAGNETIC MOMENTS OF SOME LIGHT PARTICLES

Particle	Spin	Magnetic Moment (in nuclear magnetons)
Neutron	$\frac{1}{2}$	-1.913
Proton	$\frac{1}{2}$	2.793
Deuteron	1	0.8575
Triton	$\frac{1}{2}$	2.979
Alpha particle	0	0
Photon	1	0
Neutrino	$\frac{1}{2}$	$<10^{-3}$
Electron	$\frac{1}{2}$	-1835
Positron	$\frac{1}{2}$	$+1835$
Σ and Λ hyperons	$\frac{1}{2}$ (probably)	—
K meson	0 (probably)	—
Antiproton	$\frac{1}{2}$	—
Antineutron	$\frac{1}{2}$	—

Some generalities have been deducible from the experimental results. In general, nuclei with odd mass numbers A, and thus possessing an odd number of nucleons, have half-integral spins

$$\frac{(n + \tfrac{1}{2})h}{2\pi}.$$

No value greater than 9/2 has been observed. Nuclei with odd numbers of protons and of neutrons have integral spins. On the other hand, nuclei with even mass numbers (an even number of nucleons) have integral spins; these are usually 0 or 1, although larger values have been recorded in a few cases. If the numbers of protons (Z) and neutrons ($A - Z$) are both even, the spin apparently is always zero, presumably because there is a pairing of oppositely directed spins of the respective nucleons. Inasmuch as the nucleus, like an atom, can exist in a number of excited states with quantized energies, the spins of nuclei in excited states may differ from the values of the spins in the ground state.

V.2. NUCLEAR MAGNETIC MOMENTS

An electrically charged particle moving in a closed path constitutes a current. Associated with this current is a magnetic field which can be described, at large distances, as being due to a magnetic dipole located at the loop of current. A charged particle spinning on its axis is also equivalent to a current; thus a nucleus can act like a small magnet and will possess a *magnetic dipole moment* or, simply, a *magnetic moment*. The moment of a magnet is equal to the distance between the poles multiplied by the pole strength.

The values of the magnetic moments of subatomic particles are usually expressed in terms of a unit called the *magneton*, equal to $qh/4\pi m_0 c$, where q is the magnitude of the charge, h is the Planck constant, m_0 is the rest mass of the charged particle, and c the velocity of light. If the charged particle is an electron ($q = e$), the unit is known as the *Bohr magneton*, which has the value 9.27×10^{-21} erg per gauss. If m_0 is taken as the mass of the proton, the unit is referred to as a *nuclear magneton*, having a value of 5.05×10^{-24} erg per gauss (or 3.15×10^{-12} ev per gauss). The nuclear magneton is smaller than the Bohr magneton by a factor of 1836 because the mass of the proton rather than that of the electron is involved.

Experimental values of the magnetic moments of some light particles are given in Table V.1-1. A positive sign means that the direction of the magnetic moment is the same as that produced by a rotating positive charge. A negative sign means that the moment is equivalent to a particle with a net negative charge.

According to quantum theory, the magnetic moment (expressed in magnetons) of a simple electrical particle possessing an angular momentum because of its spin should be equal to $2\sqrt{I(I + 1)}$, where I is the spin. For the electron, $I = \tfrac{1}{2}$, so that its magnetic moment should be $2\sqrt{\tfrac{1}{2}(\tfrac{1}{2} + 1)} = 1.73$ Bohr magnetons, a value that agrees very satisfactorily with the experimental value. Similarly, protons (also with spin $\frac{1}{2}$) should have a magnetic moment of 1.73 nuclear magnetons, but this is not in agreement with the experimental value of 2.793 nuclear magnetons. Further, it may be seen by reference to Table V.1-1 that the neutron, although electrically neutral and therefore presumably possessing a zero magnetic moment, surprisingly does have a magnetic moment equivalent to that of a spinning negative charge. It has been assumed, to account for this observation, that the negative charge was concentrated near the periphery of the particle and thereby overbalanced the effect of an equal positive charge nearer the center. One proposal to account for the anomalous magnetic moments of the proton and neutron is the assumption that each "particle" consists of a "bare" nucleon surrounded by a π-meson "cloud." Thus a proton would be a bare neutron surrounded by a π^+-meson cloud, whereas a neutron would be a bare proton surrounded by a π^--meson cloud (see Fig. V.2-1). In this theory it is the motion of the charged meson cloud that gives rise to the anomalous magnetic moments.

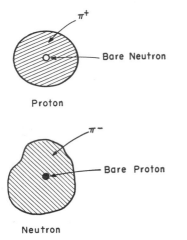

FIG. V.2-1. *Schematic representation of proposed structures of proton and neutron.*

In general, then, as the result of experiments, nuclei with nonzero spins have magnetic dipole moments μ, which are given by

$$\mu = gI\mu_0,$$

where g is known as the nuclear gyromagnetic ratio and μ_0 represents the value of the nuclear magneton.

V.3. HIGHER MOMENTS

Studies of the behavior of nuclei in magnetic fields and also of the fine structure of optical spectra indicate that many nuclei with spin greater than or equal to 1 possess electric *quadrupole moments* in addition to the magnetic dipole moment. If the positive charge of a nucleus were distributed in a completely symmetrical spherical manner, the quadrupole moment would be zero; the fact that it is frequently not zero indicates that there is an unsymmetrical, or distorted, distribution of charges. A positive quadrupole moment presumably means that the charge distribution, instead of being spherical, is drawn out to be the form of a prolate, or elongated spheroid, referred to as "cigar shaped." A negative quadrupole moment suggests that there is a flattening of the spherical distribution leading to an oblate, or flattened, spheroid, tending to a disc-like shape.

In addition, nuclei with spin greater than or equal to $\frac{3}{2}$ may have a magnetic octupole moment, and a few cases in which this has been measured are known.

Even higher electromagnetic multipole moments for nuclei with spin greater than $\frac{3}{2}$ exist.

V.4. PARITY

The concept of nuclear spin is closely tied with that of *parity*, which is concerned with the "mirror symmetry" of objects, i.e., with the right-handed or left-handed character which is interchanged as a result of reflection. Parity has no simple analogue in ordinary mechanics; the concept is concerned with some properties of the mathematical functions which are used by theoreticians to describe nuclei. It stems from a requirement that the description cannot depend on whether a system is right-handed or left-handed.

The parity of an isolated system never changes, no matter what transformations or recombinations occur within the system. This apparent fact is referred to as the law of conservation of parity. If a particle or a photon, however, enters or leaves the system, the parity of the system, which is no longer isolated, may or may not change. A corollary of the law of conservation of parity indicates that, for any atomic or nuclear system, no new physical consequence or law should result from the construction of a new system differing from the original by being a mirror twin. Consider particle 1, which is spinning about an axis AB, in Fig. V.4-1. Let particle 2 be its mirror image. The parity law predicts that there should be no observable difference between particle 1 and particle 2 which may be detected by measurements made along the direction AB. For example, if the particle is radioactive, emitting beta particles, then the number of electrons emitted in the direction toward B should equal the number emitted in the direction toward A. The reason for this is that, if particle 1 should emit more electrons toward A, then particle 2 must emit more electrons toward B, since particle 2 becomes identical with particle 1 if the former is turned upside down.

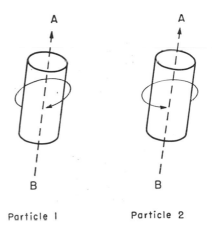

Particle 1   Particle 2

Fig. V.4-1. *Mirror twins of spinning cylinders.*

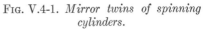

Recently a group of experiments have led to observations which indicate that the concept of parity is *not* applicable to some systems. It has been found that there *is* a distinction between oppositely spinning elementary particles. In Fig. V.4-1 the particles are represented as cylinders; however, the situation seems to correspond better to that indicated in Fig. V.4-2. Here the particles are represented as bullets, with a pointed nose, and particle 2 is again the mirror twin of particle 1. In the case represented by Figure V.4-1, no observable difference is found between the particles if particle 2 is turned upside down. In the case represented by Fig. V.4-2, however, it is evident that turning particle 2 upside down does not produce identity with particle 1: this is a result of the shape, although the spins are now in the same direction with respect to the axis AB. It is now possible to identify "right-handed" and "left-handed" particles.

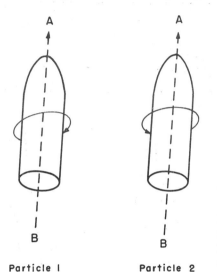

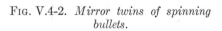

FIG. V.4-2. *Mirror twins of spinning bullets.*

The original demonstration of the inapplicability of the concept of conservation of parity (often referred to as "the overthrow of parity") was made at the National Bureau of Standards, the experiments having been suggested by Lee of Columbia and Yang of the Institute of Advanced Study, an experiment for which these scientists won a Nobel prize. Radioactive cobalt-60 (a beta emitter) was cooled to 0.01° above absolute zero to stop almost all thermal motions. The application of a magnetic field caused most of the spinning cobalt nuclei to align themselves parallel to the magnetic field (to be taken as the direction AB). The number of electrons emitted in this direction was found to be different from the number emitted in the opposite direction. A group at Argonne National Laboratory has since shown that the disintegration of the free neutron, which decays by emission of an electron to form a proton, is also a process in which the law of conservation of parity does not apply.

V.5. NUCLEAR ENERGY LEVELS

There is much evidence that quantized energy levels or states exist in nuclear systems. In particular there may be mentioned the emission of gamma rays of definite energy (or frequency) in many radioactive processes. When a nucleus is disturbed, either in the process of being formed as the result of some reaction, or by absorbing energy from radiation or a bombarding particle, it may emit one or more gamma rays of sharply defined energy (and sometimes a particle as well). Also, the emission of several groups of alpha particles, each of a definite, but different, energy, is an indication of the existence of characteristic energy states in nuclei. (There are as many as thirteen such alpha-particle groups in the case of polonium.) It may be concluded that each nucleus, no matter by what mechanism it is excited, always finds itself in one of a set of characteristic energy levels, the lowest of which is called the ground state.

The nuclear energy levels are quite analogous to the energy levels of the electrons in atoms. No two nuclear species have been found to have the same set of levels. Thus in addition to a definite mass M (or mass number A), atomic number Z, and spin I, each nuclear species is characterized by the possession of a unique set of definite energy levels. Whereas the details of the electronic states of an atom have been worked out with considerable completeness, this is far from being the case with the nuclear energy states, for the laws of force which are responsible for the stability of nuclei are not known.

From various experimental studies it has been concluded that the nuclear energy levels are relatively far apart for states of low energy (that is, near the ground state), but become closer and closer as the internal energy of the nucleus increases. At very high energies (greater than about 15 Mev above the ground state) the energy levels are so close that they may be regarded as virtually continuous.

Each excited state of a nucleus has a certain mean lifetime τ which is the period of time, on the average, during which the nucleus remains in the excited state before undergoing a change. The reciprocal of the mean life is the disintegration constant. It is customary to use instead of the latter a quantity proportional to it, called the *level width*. This has the units of energy and is defined by the relation

$$\Gamma = h/2\pi\tau. \tag{V.5-1}$$

If τ is in seconds and Γ in ev,

$$\tau\Gamma \cong 7 \times 10^{-16}. \tag{V.5-2}$$

The use of the level width is based on the Heisenberg uncertainty principle, according to which the accuracy with which energy and time can be determined in principle for a quantized system is limited by the relationship

$$(\Delta E)(\Delta t) \cong h/2\pi, \tag{V.5-3}$$

where ΔE is the uncertainty in the energy and Δt the uncertainty in time.

A state with a very short mean lifetime is poorly defined in energy and the level width is relatively large. A long-lived state, on the other hand, has a relatively large value of τ and the width is relatively small.

There is a different probability for each possible mode of transition from an excited state, and a different *partial width* Γ_i, as well as a different mean lifetime τ_i, may be defined for each process i. The *total width* of an energy level is then the sum of such individual partial widths:

$$\Gamma = \Sigma_i \Gamma_i. \tag{V.5-4}$$

As in the case of radioactivity (see § IV.3), the mean life of an unstable species is equal to the reciprocal of the decay constant, the latter representing the probability of transition per unit time. Since, as seen in Equation V.5-1, the total level width is inversely proportional to the mean lifetime of an excited state, the level width is related to the total probability that the excited state will change in unit time. Similarly, the partial level width is a measure of the probability that the given excited state will undergo the process i in unit time.

V.6. NUCLEAR RADII AND DENSITIES

Although the results of measurements of quadrupole moments indicate that most nuclei are more or less deformed, a typical nucleus can be considered as spherical to a first approximation. However, there is no single, precise definition of the "radius of a nucleus." The value is found to be dependent upon the method used for measurement, and the results of different procedures are not all in agreement. Nevertheless, no matter what method is employed, nuclear radii are smaller than atomic radii by a factor of the order of 10^4.

A fair approximation (valid to about 10 to 20 per cent) is given by the empirical formula

$$r = r_0 A^{1/3}, \qquad (V.6\text{-}1)$$

where r_0 is a constant equal to about 1.5×10^{-13} cm and A the mass number of the nucleus. From Equation V.6-1 it is seen that r_0 signifies the radius of a nucleus for which $A = 1$, that is, of the proton or neutron.

The fact that nuclear radii can be represented by an expression of the form of Equation V.6-1 leads to the concept that nuclear matter (a mixture of protons and neutrons) has a density that is nearly constant for all nuclear species. In other words, the volume $(4\pi r^3/3)$ is directly proportional to A, if the nucleus is considered as a sphere. As an example, the copper-64 isotope would have a nuclear radius of about

$$(1.5 \times 10^{-13} \text{ cm}) \, (\sqrt[3]{64}) = 6.0 \times 10^{-13} \text{ cm}.$$

Its nuclear volume would then be

$$\tfrac{4}{3}\pi (6.0 \times 10^{-13} \text{ cm})^3 \cong 9 \times 10^{-37} \text{ cm}^3.$$

Since there are 64 nucleons, each weighing approximately 1×10^{-24} gm, the nuclear density is

$$\frac{(64 \text{ nucleons})(1 \times 10^{-24} \text{ gm/nucleon})}{(9 \times 10^{-37} \text{ cm}^3)} \cong 10^{14} \text{ gm/cm}^3.$$

Of course, a uniform density of the nucleus is not possible; the nucleus must have a "surface" region over which the density falls gradually from the value at the core to zero. Accurate experiments have shown that this is the case. A plot of density versus distance from the center of the nucleus would look somewhat like the curve in Fig. V.6-1.

The radius of the neutron has recently been determined at Stanford University to be 0.8×10^{-13} cm, just about the same as that for a proton. The determination was made by measuring the scattering of 650-Mev electrons from both light and heavy hydrogen.

V.7. NUCLEAR FORCES

One of the major unsolved problems of nuclear science is to explain the nature and origin of the forces which are responsible for the strong attractions of the

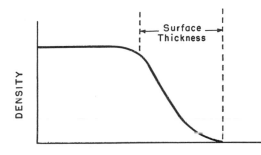

FIG. V.6-1. *The density within a nucleus as a function of the distance from the center.*

nucleons for one another and the resulting stability of nuclei. Rutherford, it will be recalled, showed experimentally that atoms consisted of an extremely dense, positively charged center with comparatively light electrons scattered through most of the volume of the atom. Therefore physicists at first believed that the force binding together the constituents of the atom was almost undoubtedly the electrostatic force discovered by Coulomb. If consideration is given only to Coulomb forces (which by far outweigh gravitational forces in magnitude), it would be anticipated that the nuclear constituents should fly apart because of the mutual repulsions between the protons contained therein. Somehow or other the presence of neutrons in nuclei prevents such a catastrophe. Thus there must exist strong *attractive* forces which hold the nucleons together and counterbalance the enormous Coulomb electrical repulsive forces.

It is certain that such forces must be essentially different from the familiar gravitational and electrostatic forces which can act over relatively long distances. The small size of the nucleus and its great stability show that the nuclear forces are *short-range forces;* they act over short distances only (of the order of 10^{-13} cm), decreasing very rapidly as the particles are separated. Within their range nuclear forces are much more effective than electrostatic forces, overcoming the mutual Coulomb repulsion between two similarly charged particles.

What we do know about nuclear forces comes mostly from mass-spectrometric data (giving binding energies) and data from scattering experiments (which tell something about the nature of the forces between the colliding particles). It may be recalled (see § I.8) that the binding energies per nucleon are nearly constant for nuclei of intermediate mass numbers. If each nucleon exerted the same attractive force on all other nucleons in its nucleus, then there would be $A(A - 1)/2$ attractive bonds among the A nucleons. The binding energy would thus increase at least as rapidly as $A^2/2$. This would require the binding energy per nucleon (B/A) to be proportional to the mass number A rather than being substantially constant as observed.

The experimental facts indicate that the nuclear forces are saturated and act between a small number of nucleons only, in much the same way that the chemical valence forces that bind the atoms together in molecules are saturated; in methane (CH_4), for example, the carbon forms stable bonds with only four hydrogen atoms and would not form a stable bond with a fifth hydrogen atom. (A Coulomb force is not saturated, since every charge interacts with all other charges, no matter how many there are.) It is probable that the maximum in the binding energy curve (see Fig. I.8-2) corresponds to saturation of the attractive nuclear forces for neighboring nucleons. The decrease in binding energy per nucleon at larger mass numbers results from a gradually increasing importance of the long-range Coulomb forces of repulsion.

The relative stability of the deuteron, composed of a proton and a neutron, shows that the force between a proton and a neutron (symbolized as a p-n force) is of appreciable magnitude. A rough comparison of the n-n (neutron-neutron) and the p-p (proton-proton) bonds can be made by studying the data in Table V.7-1. The addition of an extra neutron to a deuteron to form a tritium (H^3)

TABLE V.7-1

BINDING ENERGIES OF LIGHT NUCLEI

Nuclide	Total Binding Energy (Mev)	Binding Energy per Nucleon (Mev/nucleon)	Number of Bonds
H^2	2.21	1.10	1
H^3	8.37	2.79	3
He^3	7.63	2.54	3

nucleus, or of an extra proton to form the nucleus of He³, is accompanied by a marked increase of binding energy, partly due to the forces between two neutrons (n-n) and between two protons (p-p), respectively. The total binding energy of H³ is 8.37 Mev and that of He³ is 7.63 Mev. Both are appreciably greater than the binding energy of 2.21 Mev for the deuteron. Both H³ and He³ have two p-n bonds each, the third bond being n-n for H³ and p-p for He³. Because the binding energies are roughly the same for these two nuclei, it may be concluded that the p-p and n-n bonds have at least roughly the same energies. In order to account for detailed experimental facts, it has been found necessary to assume that the p-n force is somewhat greater than either the p-p or the n-n forces.

Scattering experiments with nuclei demonstrate the short range of nuclear forces. An effective value of 2.8×10^{-13} cm has been found for the p-p bond.

It is generally accepted that the difference between a proton and a neutron lies essentially in the fact that the former carries an electrical charge whereas the latter does not. Consider a system, for simplicity, consisting of a single proton and a single neutron, as indicated by I in Fig. V.7-1. If the positive charge of the

I   II

FIG. V.7-1. *The proton-neutron exchange system.*

proton could be transferred to the neutron (or a negative charge from neutron to proton), the condition represented by II would obtain. Although there has been an exchange of charge, resulting in a change of identity of the particles, the final state II, like the initial state I, consists of a neutron and a proton and hence has the same energy. Interpreted in terms of quantum theory, this exchange leads to an increased stability of the system; interpreted mechanically, it is equivalent to an attractive force, called an *exchange force*. It is the same type of force as has been postulated to account for the stability of chemical bonds, in which it is assumed that there is a continued physical process of exchanging (or "resonance" of) the electrons of one atom with those of the other bonded atom in the molecule.

From another point of view, this binding together of the proton and neutron may be considered as a situation in which neither state I nor state II actually exists. Rather, the actual state may be looked upon as a sort of combination or average of the individual states. When a proton and a neutron approach closely enough (within about 10^{-13} cm, the range of nuclear forces) for the attractive exchange force to be operative, neither particle is exclusively a proton or exclusively a neutron; in effect each is something intermediate. The proton and the neutron are considered to be two different charge states of a fundamental "nucleon."

In one sense the state may be described as the rapid oscillation of a positive charge between two identical particles. At one time this oscillating charge was considered to be a positron, but there is much evidence to indicate that a positron, like a electron, cannot be a nuclear constituent. In 1935 Yukawa, a Japanese physicist, postulated a new charged particle to serve in this exchange picture. His calculations led him to conclude that the particle would have a unit positive charge and a mass about 150 times that of an electron. Further, by assuming that this charged particle was unstable, expelling either an electron or a positron (in order to account for observed beta decay of nuclei), Yukawa calculated its mean life in the free state to be about 10^{-6} second. This theory would possibly have attracted little attention had not, during the next two years, mesons been discovered. The π-meson seems to fit the picture rather well, although there are very many difficulties in the theory.

In the *neutral meson theory*, the proton and neutron are regarded merely as different energy states of the same fundamental particle. The meson, which is responsible for the exchange interaction, is electrically neutral. This uncharged meson is sometimes called a *neutretto*. One advantage of the theory is that it accounts for the similarity in magnitude of p-p, n-n, and p-n forces. However, since scattering experiments and the empirically determined saturation of nuclear forces indicate that these forces are, at least in part, exchange forces, it is apparent that at least some of the mesons giving rise to nuclear forces must be charged.

The *charged meson theory* postulates the existence of positive and negative, but not neutral, mesons. The exchange between proton and neutron results from the transfer of a positive meson from the former to the latter:

$$\text{Proton} \rightleftharpoons \text{neutron} + \text{positive meson}.$$

Equivalently, it could consist in the transfer of a negative meson from the neutron to the proton:

$$\text{Neutron} \rightleftharpoons \text{proton} + \text{negative meson}.$$

In this way it is possible to account for p-n forces, since protons and neutrons can transform into each other by the emission or absorption of positive or negative mesons. But a second proton could not absorb a positive meson, because thereby it would acquire two positive charges, giving a particle which presumably does not exist. The theory does not then offer an explanation of p-p forces, supposedly of the same magnitude as p-n forces. Similarly, there is no interaction between two neutrons by this mechanism. Thus the great weakness of this theory is that it accounts only for p-n forces and does not take into consideration p-p and n-n forces.

The *symmetrical meson theory* combines the features of the above two. By making use of both charged and uncharged mesons, it can explain the interaction between like as well as unlike nucleons.

Although the meson theory seems to be attractive as a hypothesis, it has not been able to predict much that is useful. In fact, some predictions have differed from observations by a factor as much as 10^{10}. The observed interactions of mesons with nuclei is much weaker than theory would indicate.

V.8. NUCLEAR STABILITY

In connection with the problems of nuclear forces and stability, it is of interest to examine how the ratio of the number of neutrons $(A - Z)$ to the number of protons (Z) in stable nuclides varies with increasing mass number A. This may be studied in the form of a graph with the number of neutrons plotted against the

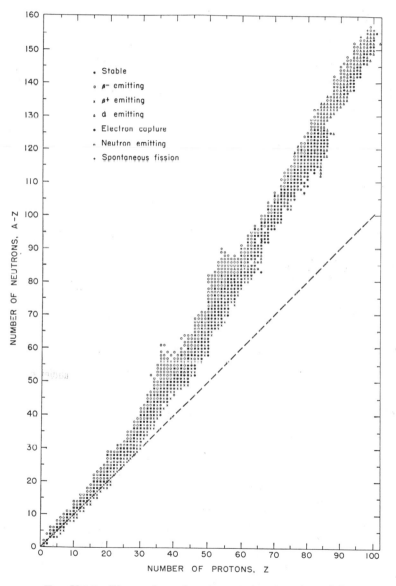

FIG. V.8-1. *The numbers of neutrons and protons in nuclei.*

number of protons, as in Fig. V.8-1, which emphasizes the general symmetry. The first observation to be made is that the stable nuclides are confined to a narrow region of the diagram. The line drawn through the origin with a slope of 45° indicates nuclei in which the number of neutrons is equal to the number of protons. For stable isotopes below about $A = 20$, the neutron-to-proton ratio is close to unity. This is what is to be expected if the p-p and n-n forces are approximately equal while the p-n forces are somewhat larger.

For nuclei above $A = 20$, stability is apparently obtained only when the neutron-to-proton ratio exceeds unity. The number of neutrons must exceed the number of protons. For the heaviest elements the neutron-to-proton ratio becomes greater than 1.5.

Presumably this may be explained by the fact that, as the atomic number increases, more and more protons are packed into the nucleus. The Coulomb force of repulsion among these protons does not exhibit the saturation character of nuclear forces. As the number of protons increases, the electrostatic force of repulsion grows rapidly. More neutrons must be added to supply large forces of attraction from the p-n and n-n combinations in order to overcome or compensate for the large repulsion. This is seen in Fig. V.8-1 by the continuing increase in vertical distance, with mass number, of the region of stable nuclei above the line indicating equal numbers of protons and neutrons. Nonetheless, as may be seen from Fig. I.8-2, beyond about $Z = 50$ the electrostatic repulsion has increased to such an extent that the binding energy per nucleon decreases steadily with increasing mass number.

Further examination of the data shows that stable nuclei containing even numbers of both protons and neutrons are much more common than any others. Stable nuclei with an odd number of protons and an even number of neutrons are about as common as nuclei with an even number of protons and an odd number of neutrons. It is only rarely that stable nuclei with an odd number of both protons and neutrons are found (see Table V.8-1).

TABLE V.8-1

NUMBER OF STABLE NUCLEAR TYPES

Number of Neutrons:	Number of Protons	
	Even	Odd
Even	162	52
Odd	56	4

An interpretation of these results has been based on the supposition that stable nuclear states or shells exist in the nucleus in analogy to the shells of electrons in the atom. A closed, or complete, nuclear state consists of two protons and two neutrons, the spins of each pair being oppositely directed. If each nucleon interacts strongly only with nucleons in the same state, but weakly with nucleons in other states, the forces acquire the property of saturation which is characteristic of nuclear binding.

Nuclei consisting of closed shells should be exceptionally stable. It may be seen from Fig. I.8-2 that the alpha particle (one closed shell), carbon-12 (three closed shells) and oxygen-16 (four closed shells) are relatively more stable than surrounding isotopes. (The beryllium-8 isotope, which should contain two closed shells, is an exception, being highly unstable and, when formed, breaking up almost immediately into two alpha particles.)

For a nucleus to consist entirely of such closed states of two protons and two neutrons, there would be required equal numbers of protons and neutrons. As seen above, this is possible only for elements with $A < 20$. With increasing mass number, the number of neutrons must be increased if stability is to be maintained. Next to a closed shell of two neutrons and two protons, it would seem that a combination of two neutrons with opposite spins would be preferred, analogous to the covalent bond. Thus nuclei with even numbers of both protons and neutrons should be stable, in agreement with the predominance of such nuclei over all others, as given in Table V.8-1.

In addition to the normal stability of even-even nuclei due to the pairing of protons and neutrons, there is evidence for believing that nuclei containing 2, 8, 20, 50, 82, or 126 nucleons of the *same* kind are particularly stable. These numbers, often called *magic numbers*, appear to be associated with some form of shell structure in the nucleus. On the basis of determination of quadrupole moments (see § V.3), only those nuclei which correspond to closed shell numbers of protons and/or neutrons are known to be spherical; others are more or less deformed.

V.9. NUCLEAR MODELS

On the basis of the little knowledge we have concerning nuclear forces, several models of nuclei have been constructed to explain their properties. Niels Bohr and J. Wheeler in 1939 proposed a model in which the nucleus was considered to be similar to a drop of incompressible fluid. The nucleons were imagined to behave something like the molecules within a drop of liquid. The thermal agitation of the molecules in the droplet had a counterpart in the kinetic energy possessed by the nucleons. The energy required to evaporate a drop was analogous to the total binding energy of the nucleus. The constancy of the nuclear density ($\sim 10^{14}$ gm/cm^3 or $\sim 10^{38}$ nucleons/cm^3) is just what is to be expected if the nucleus behaves like a liquid with short-range forces operating between the constituent particle.

In a liquid the cohesive forces between molecules are short-range forces, operating between a given molecule and those immediately adjacent to it. Similar considerations apply to the forces between nucleons (see § V.7). This attractive force leads to a contribution to the energy of the nucleus which is proportional to the number A of nucleons present:

$$\text{Attractive energy} = aA, \qquad (V.9\text{-}1)$$

where a is a constant.

In stating that the attractive energy is proportional to the mass number A, it is tacitly assumed that every nucleon has the same access to other nucleons. Actually, the nucleons at the surface will be less tightly bound than those in the interior of the nucleus, so that the energy given by Equation V.9-1 is an over-estimate by an amount which depends on the surface area (see § V.6 and Fig. V.6-1). The larger this area, the greater will be the number of nucleons which are not surrounded completely by others. Because the effect is similar to that which causes the surface tension in a liquid, it is called the surface tension effect. Since (see § V.6) the nuclear radius is proportional to $A^{1/3}$ and the surface area of a sphere is proportional to the square of the radius, we have

$$\text{Surface tension energy} = -bA^{2/3}, \tag{V.9-2}$$

where b is a constant. Just as a liquid drop tends to assume a spherical shape under the action of surface tension, the unsaturation of the nuclear forces at the surface makes a sphere the most stable configuration for a heavy nucleus.

On the basis of the model (in which other, smaller, corrections were made) Bohr and Wheeler have shown that there will be a certain critical size for nuclei, depending on Z^2/A, above which the force of electrostatic repulsion will be greater than the forces holding the nucleus together. The critical size was calculated to be in the neighborhood of $Z = 100$.

The liquid-drop model has been a helpful guide to thinking about the nucleus. A good description of fission was obtained. However, the model has not been too helpful in studying other nuclear phenomena, such as in the case of nuclear reactions in which a projectile has a very high kinetic energy. The liquid-drop model, further, is inherently incapable of accounting for the magic numbers.

Another model, the nuclear shell model, has been envisioned which makes essentially the same assumption for nuclear particles as was made for electrons in explaining atomic structure. Each nucleon is assumed to move independently in a spherically symmetric but limited field of force resulting from the combined effects of the other $A - 1$ nucleons.[1] As in the electronic case, nuclear orbits are characterized by a set of quantum numbers, and the corresponding energy levels are filled independently either with neutrons or with protons. Proton and neutron levels characterized by the same quantum numbers would not exactly coincide because of the Coulomb forces acting only on the protons and shifting these levels to higher energy. By a proper choice of the assumed potential and a consideration of other factors, it becomes possible to obtain closed shells corresponding to the recognized magic numbers.

The shell model has been very helpful in understanding many regularities in the chart of nuclei. Certain successful predictions have also been made regarding the expected spins and various moments of nuclei. However, the shell model provides no information on the absolute separations of nuclear energy levels nor on binding energies. It remains a fairly crude model.

[1]In contrast to the situation with atomic electrons, the nucleus contains no massive central body which can act as a center of force.

CHAPTER VI

THE REACTIONS OF NUCLEI

VI.1. NUCLEAR REACTIONS

In 1919 Lord Rutherford observed the first nuclear reaction when he exposed nitrogen gas to alpha particles emitted from radium. He found that long-range protons were emitted as a result of the ensuing interaction with the nitrogen nucleus:

$$_7N^{14} + {}_2He^4 \rightarrow {}_8O^{17} + {}_1H^1. \qquad (VI.1-1)$$

Since then over a thousand nuclear reactions have been studied. In fact, the science of the artificial transmutation of the elements has become a large and important branch of physics.

A nuclear reaction (as distinguished from a radioactive process) is a process in which a nucleus reacts in consequence of an external stimulus — another nucleus, an elementary particle, a photon — to produce one or more other nuclei and, possibly, other elementary particles or photons. It has been demonstrated that nuclei can be changed, in various ways, by bombardment or "atom smashing" with projectiles of nuclear size or with gamma rays. The target nucleus may (1) emit a small number of nucleons (often just one), (2) emit many nucleons, either singly or in small groups, (3) absorb the projectile and emit gamma rays, (4) break up into two or more pieces (as in nuclear fission), or (5) emit mesons. Generally this all takes places in a time of the order of 10^{-12} second or less.

When a target nucleus and a projectile come together, two basic types of events can occur as a result of their interaction: (1) the nuclei may be scattered by each other without a change in the total energy or in the internal structures; (2) energy may be exchanged and the internal structures altered. A nuclear reaction may then be said to have occurred.

In describing a nuclear reaction, it makes a great deal of difference whether the kinetic energy of the bombarding particle is (1) much smaller than or (2) much greater than the binding energy of the nucleons in the struck nucleus. In the first case the projectile, on entering the nucleus, shares its energy with the other nucleons and soon loses its identity. The interaction is considered as being between the nucleus as a whole and the incident particle.

When the energy of the incident particle is very high, the incoming projectile is moving so fast that the nucleons in the target nucleus may be considered as standing still. The incoming particle may pass right through the nucleus, so that there is no reaction at all, or it may have an interaction with a single nucleon (or a small number of them). It is not then a reaction between the projectile and the nucleus as a whole.

To aid in considering the nature and type of a nuclear reaction, a convenient, compact notation has been devised. The bombarded isotope is placed before parentheses. Inside the parentheses are placed the projectile and then the ejected particle or particles, a comma being used for the separation. Finally, the product isotope is placed after the parentheses. Thus the pioneer nuclear reaction (Equation VI.1-1) is written as $_7N^{14}(\alpha,p)_8O^{17}$, or simply, since the symbol of the chemical element really tells us the nuclear charge Z, as $N^{14}(\alpha,p)O^{17}$. The α symbolizes an alpha particle, the p a proton. Other symbols employed are e^- or β^- for an electron, e^+ or β^+ for a positron, γ for gamma ray, n for neutron, and d for deuteron. A reaction of the type of Equation VI.1-1 is called an (α,p) reaction.

VI.2. ENERGETICS OF NUCLEAR REACTIONS

After Rutherford's discovery, attempts were made to accomplish or induce nuclear transformations by the controlled acceleration of various kinds of nuclear particles. The first successful transmutation induced by energetic protons was accomplished by Cockcroft and Walton in 1931. Protons were accelerated by a potential of 280 kev and were allowed to impinge on a target of lithium. It was found that alpha particles with a range, in air, of 8.4 cm were emitted as a result of the reaction

$$_1H^1 + {}_3Li^7 \rightarrow {}_2He^4 + {}_2He^4. \tag{VI.2-1}$$

The energy of the alpha particles represented an energy of about 8.5 Mev each, many times the energy of the bombarding protons.

The chemist adds to his equation expressing a given chemical reaction a term, the heat of reaction, expressing the gain or loss of heat. Thus

$$2H_2 + O_2 \rightarrow 2H_2O + 136 \text{ kcal}$$

means that 136 kcal are evolved when two gram-molecules of hydrogen and one gram-molecule of oxygen combine to form 2 gram-molecules of water. Heat may also be absorbed. The evaluation or absorption of heat is described by the terms exothermic or endothermic reaction, respectively.

In the same way, physicists add a term, called the nuclear energy change and universally represented by the symbol Q, to an equation such as Equation VI.2-1. Thus

$$_3Li^7 + {}_1H^1 \rightarrow {}_2He^4 + {}_2He^4 + (Q = 17.3 \text{ Mev}). \tag{VI.2-2}$$

Like the chemist, the physicist calls such reactions exothermic or endothermic depending upon whether Q is positive or negative, respectively.

The isotopic weights involved in Equation VI.2-2 are 7.018232, 4.003873, and 1.008145 amu, respectively, for Li⁷, He⁴, and H¹. There is an excess of 0.018631 amu on the left-hand side, equivalent in energy by Einstein's mass-energy relationship to $Q = 17.3$ Mev. It would be expected as a result of the reaction that each helium nucleus will acquire $\frac{1}{2}(17.3) = 8.63$ Mev. This compares very favorably with the observed value of about 8.5 Mev. The mass deficiency means that an energy of 17.3 Mev was set free by the insignificant amount of kinetic energy of the incident proton.

However, despite the fact that each reaction VI.2-2 sets free so much more energy than is possessed by the incident proton, the probability of the transmutation is so small (since so few of the accelerated protons lead to a successful reaction) that no total gain in the release of energy can be anticipated. Thus a reaction such as Equation VI.2-2 cannot be utilized as a practical process for the liberation of nuclear energy. A large amount of energy is used in getting the beam of protons, but by far the vast majority of the protons will not react with the lithium nuclei. The net effect is that more energy is used than would be obtained.

VI.3. NUCLEAR POTENTIAL BARRIERS

If a projectile used to bombard a nucleus is positively charged, there exists a Coulomb force of repulsion or repulsive Coulomb barrier between the two. It was this barrier which caused the scattering of alpha particles in Rutherford's experiments (see § I.5) and led him to propose his picture of a nuclear atom. It

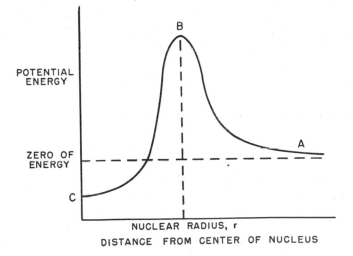

FIG. VI.3-1. *Hypothetical potential-energy curve for the interaction between a nucleus and an alpha particle.*

was also this barrier which had to be surmounted by the alpha particles that Rutherford shot at the nitrogen nuclei before they could react.

The emission of alpha particles from radioactive isotopes is itself an indication that such particles can exist, even if only for an extremely short time, within such nuclei. The interaction between a radioactive nucleus and an alpha particle, both inside and outside the nucleus, can be represented pictorially by a potential-energy curve, such as that in Fig. VI.3-1. The rising portion of the curve, from A to B, indicates the increasing repulsion as an alpha particle approaches the nucleus. The sharp fall from B to C, which is essentially the region within the nucleus and is due to the nuclear attractive forces, implies the existence of the alpha particle there.

The height of the barrier at B is equal to the potential difference, $2Ze^2/r$, through which the alpha particle moves; here Ze is the charge on the nucleus, $2e$ the charge on the alpha, and r the radius. An alpha particle with an energy less than this maximum will be unable to enter the nucleus. If the alpha particle is to unite with the target nucleus, it must possess an energy in excess of this height, so that it can reach a region where the short-range attractive nuclear force becomes effective.

The height of the barrier for a given nucleus depends on the charge of the incident particle. The height V around a nucleus of charge Ze and radius r_1 for an incident particle of charge ze and radius r_2 may be estimated as the energy of Coulomb repulsion when the two particles are just in contact:

$$V = \frac{Zze^2}{r_1 + r_2}. \tag{VI.3-1}$$

If the incident particle were a proton or a deuteron, the barrier height would be only about one-half as high as for alpha particles, so that the probability of such a projectile entering a given nucleus is larger than for the entry of an alpha particle. The height of the barrier does not increase directly as the atomic number Z of the bombarded nucleus for a given projectile, because the nuclear radius is a function of Z. (Approximately, r is proportional to $Z^{1/3}$.) If a neutron were the incident particle, no Coulomb barrier would exist. It is indeed the case that neutrons of very low energy can enter most nuclei with comparative ease.

VI.4. THE COMPOUND NUCLEUS

In 1936 Niels Bohr (and independently Breit and Wigner) developed a statistical theory of nuclear reactions which has been very successful in explaining many features of reactions induced by particles of moderate energies (up to about 40 Mev). The nucleus is regarded as a densely packed system of nucleons. The distances between the nucleons are of the same order of magnitude as the range of the nuclear forces (see § V.7), and the interaction energies between nucleons are of the same order of magnitude as the kinetic energies of the incident particles.

When an incident particle hits and coalesces with a target nucleus, the resultant is called a *compound nucleus*. This product may be a stable nucleus or one which is unstable. In general, the compound nucleus is in a state of high energy (excited state) above its ground state. The excitation energy (that is, the energy above the ground state of the compound nucleus) is nearly equal to the kinetic energy of the captured particle plus its binding energy in the compound nucleus. Immediately after formation of the compound nucleus, its excitation energy may be regarded as being concentrated in the captured projectile. As a result of collisions and interactions with the closely packed nucleons within the nucleus, however, the incident particle loses some of its energy and is held by the nuclear forces. The additional energy introduced by the projectile is very rapidly distributed among and shared by the nucleons present in the compound nucleus before the incident particle can be re-emitted. The distribution of energy presumably takes place in a random way.

The compound nucleus remains in its excited state a relatively long time before passing to a more stable configuration, because a large number of collisions is required before enough energy is likely to be "accidentally" concentrated on one nucleon or a group of nucleons to allow escape from the nuclear binding forces. It appears that the average life of a compound nucleus varies from about 10^{-16} to 10^{-12} second, depending on how highly excited it is. This is a lifetime which is very long compared to the time required for a fast particle to traverse a distance equal to a nuclear diameter. For example, even for a slow neutron with speed equal to 10^5 cm/sec to cross a nuclear diameter, say 10^{-12} cm, the time is $(10^{-12}$ cm$)/(10^5$ cm/sec$) = 10^{-17}$ second.

The compound nucleus may lose its excitation energy in various ways. It may emit a single light particle which may or may not be the same as the projectile. It may emit a small number of light particles. It may emit one or more gamma rays (radiative capture reactions). It may break up into two or more pieces, as occurs in fission.

Bohr assumed that the way in which a compound nucleus disintegrates is independent of the manner in which it was formed, depending only on the properties of the compound nucleus itself, such as the energy and angular momentum. Every possible decay has its own probability. Sometimes one decay process will be highly favored. On the other hand, several processes with about the same probabilities may compete with one another.

Consider a particular compound nucleus, Al^{27}, in an excited state. It may be formed in various ways, such as

$$
\begin{aligned}
Na^{23} + \alpha \\
Mg^{25} + d \\
Mg^{26} + p \\
Al^{27} + \gamma
\end{aligned}
\quad\longrightarrow\quad (Al^{27})^*,
$$

where the asterisk indicates the excited condition. The excitation energy depends upon the nature and energy of the incident particle. Once formed, the excited nucleus may decay in a variety of ways. For example,

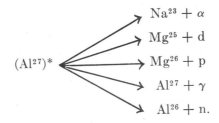

$$(Al^{27})^* \begin{cases} Na^{23} + \alpha \\ Mg^{25} + d \\ Mg^{26} + p \\ Al^{27} + \gamma \\ Al^{26} + n. \end{cases}$$

All of these modes of decay compete with one another. Very often one particular process will have such a high probability of occurrence that all the others are effectively ruled out. The Bohr theory is in agreement with experimental observations that the bombardment of a given nuclide with a given type of nuclear particle usually leads to a variety of products.

For elements of high atomic number the potential barrier caused by electrostatic forces is high. It may be expected that under such conditions the probability of emission of a charged particle is low and that preferentially a neutron or a gamma ray will be emitted. For isotopes of small atomic number, on the other hand, neutrons are often more strongly bound in the compound nucleus than are protons; since the energy barrier for the latter is then not relatively too high, the ejection of a proton may be expected to occur with a high probability. When the energy of a compound nucleus is not sufficient to permit the expulsion of a nucleon, its excess energy may be emitted in the form of gamma radiation. Another possibility is the expulsion of an electron or positron, requiring the transformation within the nucleus of a neutron into a proton or of a proton into a neutron, respectively; this change is generally slow as compared with the direct emission of a particle or of a gamma-ray photon.

At very high excitation energies, induced by particles with kinetic energies greater than about 40 Mev, the mean life of the compound nucleus is greatly decreased. It then becomes questionable, based as the concept is on a rapid exchange of energy among the nucleons, whether the model of a compound nucleus can be considered at all. More and more complex reactions may be expected to occur with higher and higher energies of the incident particles. For example, mesons may be produced. The interaction at these very high energies appears to be between the incoming particle and one or two nucleons, rather than between the projectile and the entire nucleus.

VI.5. THE FISSION REACTION

The ineffectiveness of ordinary nuclear projectiles, such as alpha particles and protons, lies essentially in their electric charge, which causes them to lose energy while passing through atoms and prevents them from coming sufficiently close to the charged target nuclei. Better results are obtained with uncharged neutrons. Only one isotope, helium-4, will not react with neutrons of moderate energy. With this one exception, every isotope reacts with bombarding neutrons. Of course, the probability of reaction with the neutron varies greatly with different materials and with the energy of the neutron.

The process of capture of a neutron by a nucleus may lead to new stable or radioactive isotopes of either the bombarded nuclide or of a nuclide near it in the periodic table. The type of reaction induced depends largely on the kinetic energy of the incident neutron. The disintegration occurring may consist in the ejection from the compound nucleus of a gamma ray (by far the commonest process), proton, alpha particle, additional neutrons, or many particles; or it may result in fission.

The fission[1] reaction, discovered in 1939, was the first to offer the feasibility of practical utilization of nuclear energy. Fission is the term used to describe the splitting of a heavy nucleus into two roughly equal parts, called fission fragments. The importance of this reaction is based on two facts. First, the process is associated with the release of relatively large amounts of energy, about 200 Mev in the case of uranium for each nucleus reacting. The released energy can be several billion times the energy carried by the incident neutron which initiates fission. Secondly, the reaction, initiated by neutrons, is accompanied by the liberation of more neutrons which are capable of causing fission of other fissionable nuclei. It is possible, then, under suitable conditions, for the process to be self-sustaining and for the energy to be liberated continuously.

The magnitude of the energy liberated in fission can be calculated in several ways. Using uranium-235 as an example, if the compound nucleus uranium-236 is divided by the fission into two nuclei each of mass number 118, the binding energy per nucleon increases from about 7.6 to about 8.5 Mev. This is an increase of about 0.9 Mev/nucleon. For the single uranium-236 nucleus this amounts to (0.9 Mev/nucleon)(236 nucleons) $\cong$ 210 Mev.

Again, the isotopic mass of uranium-235 is 235.117496 amu and the mass of the neutron is 1.008986 amu, making a sum of 236.126482 amu for the total mass of the interacting particles. The fission products obtained in greatest yield have mass numbers of 95 and 139, and it may be assumed that two neutrons are liberated in the fission process. Isotopic weights corresponding to stable nuclides having mass numbers 95 and 139 are 94.935800 (for zirconium) and 138.952970 (for lanthanum), respectively. Thus the sum of the stable products after fission are 235.906562. The difference in mass between reactants and products is thus 236.126482 − 235.906562 = 0.21992 amu or (0.21992 amu)(931 Mev/amu) = 206 Mev. The average energy will be the weighted mean for the thirty or more different ways in which the uranium-235 nucleus splits.

---

[1] A word borrowed from the biologists.

Most of the energy is released in the primary process of fission itself. A smaller amount of energy is liberated in the radioactive decay of the fission fragments to form stable residual isotopes. The total energy released appears as the kinetic energies of the fission fragments, electrons, gamma-ray photons, neutrons, and neutrinos. Eventually a great portion of the energy appears as heat.

From the extent of the ionization produced by the fission fragments, it has been estimated that their energy is about 165 Mev, which is by far the largest fraction of the energy available from fission. Direct calorimetric measurements give the heat energy liberated as 175 Mev. It has been estimated that the total amount of energy produced by decay of the fission fragments to form stable nuclei is about 27 Mev. Of this about 9 Mev is energy of the beta particles, 7 Mev is energy of the gamma radiation, and the remainder is carried off by the neutrinos which accompany beta emission. In addition, some 8 Mev of the fission energy are associated with the instantaneous gamma radiation, and 5 Mev with the fission neutrons. An approximate energy balance is given in Table VI.5-1.

TABLE VI.5-1

DISTRIBUTION OF THE ENERGY OF FISSION

Kind of Energy	Magnitude (Mev)
Kinetic energy of fission fragments	165
Energy of beta decay	9
Energy of gamma decay	7
Energy of neutrinos	11
Energy of fission neutrons	5
Instantaneous gamma-ray energy	8
	205 (total)

Now

$$1 \text{ Mev} = 1.60 \times 10^6 \text{ erg} = 1.60 \times 10^{-13} \text{ watt-second}$$

Since the energy of the neutrinos (11 Mev) is not available, it is thus seen that the fission of a single uranium-235 nucleus is accompanied by the liberation of

$$(194 \text{ Mev})(1.60 \times 10^{-13} \text{ watt-second/Mev}) = 3.11 \times 10^{-11} \text{ watt-second}.$$

In other words it requires 3.2×10^{10} fissions to release 1 watt-second of energy, so that fissions at the rate of 3.2×10^{10} per second would yield 1 watt of power. Since 1 gm of uranium-235 contains

$$\frac{6.02 \times 10^{23} \text{ atoms/gram atom}}{235 \text{ gm/gram atom}} = 2.6 \times 10^{21} \text{ atoms/gm},$$

the energy produced by its complete fission would be 8.3×10^{10} watt-seconds or 2.3×10^4 kilowatt-hours, or nearly 1 megawatt-day. The fission of all the atoms in 1 gm of uranium-235 per day would yield 1 megawatt of power.

Bohr and Wheeler worked out a theory for the fission process based on the liquid-drop model (§ V.9). It is known that a liquid drop, normally stable, can be made to break up if mechanical vibrations of large enough amplitude can be set up in it. The energy needed to excite a nucleus into a violent and irregular motion is supplied by the absorbed neutron. The oscillations may distort the nuclear droplet into an unstable shape with consequent disruption (see Fig. VI.5-1). (In the case of uranium-235 about 85 per cent of the thermal neutron captures are effective in this manner.)

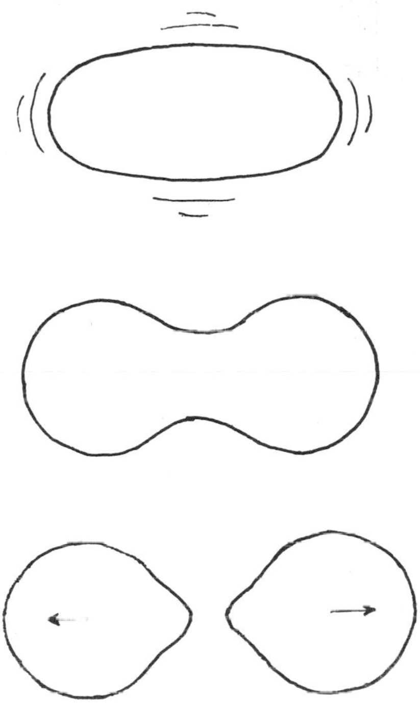

The first instance of fission was brought about by slow neutrons interacting with uranium-235, which makes up about 0.7 per cent of the isotopic composition of natural uranium. The more abundant uranium-238 requires fast neutrons, with energies exceeding 1 Mev, to produce fission.

In the process of fission the nucleus breaks into two fission fragments in many different ways, any one of which may occur within about 5×10^{-13} second after the capture of the neutron. More than thirty modes of fission of uranium-235 have been detected, giving about sixty products, with mass numbers rang-

Fig. VI.5-1. *Water-droplet model of the fission process.*

ing from about 72 (probably an isotope of zinc, $Z = 30$) to 158 (probably an isotope of samarium, $Z = 62$). However, the great majority of these fragments fall into two groups (see Fig. VI.5-2), with mass numbers in the range of 85 to 104 (the light group) and 130 to 149 (the heavy group), separated by a very pronounced minimum. The most probable type of fission, representing nearly 6.4 per cent of the total, gives products with mass numbers 95 and 139. Only about 0.01 per cent of the nuclei undergoing fission break up into two equal fragments. (This symmetrical fission becomes more probable, although still comparatively rare, as neutrons of increasing energy are employed.) Both fission fragments are initially highly ionized, carrying with them only about one-half of their full complement of orbital electrons, the others being lost as a result of the initial outward impulse. As the fragments move away from the site of fission, capture and loss of electrons is a process of major importance.

The distribution of the neutrons accompanying fission indicates that they are ejected from the fission fragments and not from the compound nucleus. In other

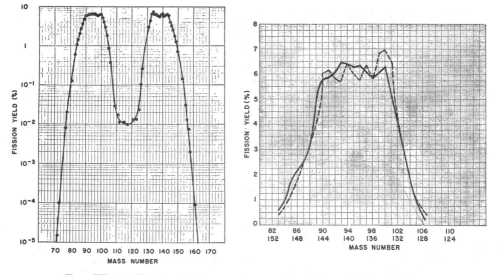

Fig. VI.5-2. *Fission-yield curve for uranium-235 and slow neutrons.*

words, the latter first breaks up into two parts, each of which probably has too many neutrons for stability, as well as sufficient energy to make neutron emission possible. Each excited, unstable nucleus consequently expels one or more neutrons, probably within 10^{-12} second, in an attempt to attain or approach stability. The instantaneous gamma rays accompanying fission are probably emitted at the same time. On the average, the neutrons produced in fission have energies of the order of 1 to 2 Mev.

Over 99 per cent of the neutrons produced in fission are released within an extremely short interval of time; these are called prompt neutrons. In addition, about 0.65 per cent of the neutrons derived from fission of uranium-235 are *delayed neutrons*, the emission of which continues for some time (up to several minutes) after fission occurs. The delayed neutrons do not arise in the primary fission process, but are emitted by unstable nuclides somewhere along the decay chains by which fission fragments achieve stability. Some of these decay products are in a state of such high excitation that neutron emission successfully competes with gamma-ray or beta-ray emission which might normally be expected of such excited nuclei.

On the average, 2.47 prompt neutrons are produced by the thermal neutron fission of uranium-235. The number is not an integer because the uranium-235 nucleus splits in more than thirty different ways. Although the number of neutrons expelled in any individual act of fission must be integral, the average is not a whole number.

Because of the fact that the neutron excess $(A - 2Z)$ required for stability is much greater in the region of the heavy elements than in the region of the fission products (see Fig. V.8-1), the fission fragments have neutron excesses far greater than the stable isotopes of the same elements. These fission fragments achieve stability through a succession of beta decays, thereby increasing the nuclear charge to make the numbers of protons and neutrons more equal. (Some, as just mentioned, are the sources of the delayed neutrons.) Some chains with as many as six successive beta decays are known. Although some fission decay chains are longer and some shorter, on the average each such chain consists of three stages of decay before a stable species is formed. Since there are some sixty different radioactive nuclei produced directly in a given sample in which fission is occurring, and since each of these nuclei is, on the average, the precursor of two others, after a short time about 180 radioactive species may be present.

Some heavy nuclei have been found to undergo *spontaneous fission*, dividing without bombardment by particles from an external source. It has been postulated that the disintegration constants for the spontaneous fission of the transplutonium elements are so high, and thus the half-lives so small, that this may account, at least in part, for their absence in nature.

VI.6. CROSS SECTIONS

Like radioactivity, the mechanisms involved in the production of nuclear reactions by means of nuclear projectiles are random in character and may be treated by the methods used in studies of probability. The efficiency or the probability of occurrence of a nuclear reaction can be defined experimentally in terms of the number of particles emitted, or of nuclei undergoing transformation, out of some total number for a specified number of incident particles. A more general, uniform procedure that has been widely adopted is to express the relative efficiency by means of a quantity called the *nuclear cross section*, usually represented by the symbol σ. It represents the *effective* area of cross section presented by a single nucleus of a given species for a particular reaction. Statistically it can be pictured as the area of an *imaginary* circular disc associated with each nucleus in a thin foil so that the reaction occurs if the incident particle passes through it.[1] When the efficiency of the process is high, the nuclear cross section will be large; when the efficiency is low, the cross section will be small. In general, the value of the cross section depends upon the specific reaction (that is, the natures of the nuclear particles involved) and the energy of the bombarding particle.

Each kind of nuclear process may be regarded as having a cross section for each nucleus and each incident particle. Thus, for neutrons, say, there is a cross section for elastic scattering, another for inelastic scattering, one for radiative capture (n,γ) reactions, for proton emission (n,p), for fission, and so on. A given nucleus, such as lithium-7, for example, will then have different cross sections for the reactions $\text{Li}^7(p,n)\text{Be}^7$, $\text{Li}^7(p,\alpha)\text{He}^4$ and $\text{Li}^7(p,d)\text{Li}^6$, which occur simul-

[1]There is no guarantee that an incident particle headed straight for a nucleus will penetrate it at all. It depends on the nucleus and the projectile.

taneously in different Li^7 nuclei in the target. The *total* cross section of a nucleus for a given incident particle is simply the sum of the cross sections for each of the various possible processes.

Let I represent the number of incident particles per unit time per unit area of target. Let N be the number of target nuclei per unit target area and A the number of these nuclei which undergo reaction in the specified time. Then, since σ is the effective area of reaction per nucleus, the effective area per square centimeter of surface presented by the target material is σN; that is, σN is the fraction of the surface which is capable of taking part in the reaction in the given time. Since I is the number of incident particles per unit time per unit area falling on the target surface, σNI must be the number, A, of nuclei actually reacting per unit time. Thus

$$A = \sigma NI, \qquad (VI.6\text{-}1)$$

so that σ is given by

$$\sigma = A/NI. \qquad (VI.6\text{-}2)$$

All the quantities on the right-hand side are measurable.

The average diameter of a nucleus can be taken to be about 10^{-12} cm. Thus the geometrical cross section of the nucleus, considered as a sphere, is given by πr^2 or approximately 10^{-24} cm². A unit called the barn and equal to 10^{-24} cm² has been adopted. Experimental values of nuclear cross sections are generally of the order of 1 barn, but they are known to vary from 10^{-8} to more than 10^4 barns for different reactions.

The quantity

$$\Sigma \equiv N_v \sigma \qquad (VI.6\text{-}3)$$

is called the *macroscopic cross section*, in contradistinction to σ, which is termed the *microscopic cross section*. Here N_v is the number of nuclei per unit volume. It will be seen that Σ represents the total cross section of all the nuclei in the unit volume.

If ρ is the density of the elementary target material (gm/cm³) and A its atomic weight, then ρ/A is the number of gram atoms per cm³. If N_0 ($= 6.02 \times 10^{23}$ atoms/gm atom) denotes Avogadro's number, the number of individual atoms per cm³ is given by

$$N = \rho N_0/A, \qquad (VI.6\text{-}4)$$

so that

$$\Sigma = (\rho N_0/A)\sigma. \qquad (VI.6\text{-}5)$$

If the material contains several nuclear species, the total macroscopic cross section is given as the sum of the individual values for each kind.

The cross sections for the capture of slow neutrons (i.e., with an energy less than about 0.5 ev) is in many cases much greater than the geometric cross section determined from the nuclear radius. For example, cadmium has a cross section of 2900 barns and gadolinium of 30,000 barns. These values are average cross sections for the natural mixture of isotopes. In cadmium, for example, the cross

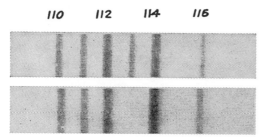

Fɪɢ. VI.6-1. *The disappearance of the cadmium-113 isotope upon bombardment by neutrons. The upper photograph shows the mass spectrum before neutron bombardment, and the lower one before.* [*Reprinted from A. J. Dempster, Phys. Rev., 71: 829 (1947).*]

section for the capture of slow neutrons by cadmium-113 is about 23,000 barns. Striking proof that cadmium-113 absorbs neutrons very strongly was obtained by Dempster. Natural cadmium was exposed to a beam of low neutrons. After some time specimens of reacted and unreacted metal were examined in the mass spectrograph, with the results shown in Fig. VI.6-1. In the neutron-bombarded sample there is barely a trace of cadmium 113, whereas the proportion of cadmium-114 has increased as a result of the $Cd^{113}(n,\gamma)Cd^{114}$ reaction.

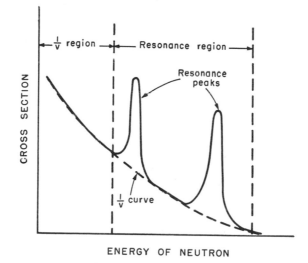

Fɪɢ. VI.6-2. *Schematic representation of the variation of the cross section for capture of a neutron as a function of the neutron energy.*

For neutrons having energies in the slow or thermal region and somewhat above, the cross sections for many substances are found to obey a $1/v$ law, that is, the cross section for the capture of neutrons varies inversely with the velocity of the neutron. Physically this may be interpreted as an indication that the capture of the neutron is proportional to the length of time which the neutron spends in the vicinity of the absorbing nucleus.

However, in practically all elements there are deviations from the $1/v$ law in one or more energy ranges due to the existence of what are called *resonance levels*. A small difference in the energy of the neutron may cause a very large change in the capture cross section. For example, uranium-238 has a highly important cross section of several thousand barns for neutrons of about 5-ev energy. If the neutron entering the nucleus has an energy which will just bring the compound nucleus into one of its own energy levels, the probability of capture will be particularly high. Reactions occurring in this way are called resonance processes. In such cases if a cross section is measured as a function of the energy of the neutron, then a curve such as the one in Fig. VI.6-2 may be obtained; it appears to be a $1/v$ curve upon which are superimposed the resonance peaks. Such curves are valuable in determining the excitation energies of nuclei. (Similar resonances have been observed among the lighter elements for reactions with protons, deuterons, and alpha particles. These are not found for heavier elements because of the large Coulomb barrier.) Resonances may occur not only for capture reactions, but for other processes, such as scattering, as well.

At very high energies of the bombarding particles (in the Mev range), the total cross sections for neutron reactions are very small for all elements, usually being less than 5 barns in magnitude. Under these conditions, the principal contributions to the observed cross sections are due to scattering.

VI.7. NUCLEAR DECAY SCHEMES

The gamma rays emitted by radioactive materials result from the fact that the daughter nucleus is in an excited state and the excitation energy is lost by

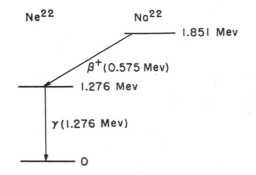

FIG. VI.7-1. *Simplified decay scheme for sodium-22.*

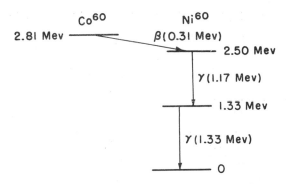

FIG. VI.7-2. *Simplified decay scheme for cobalt*-60.

emission of the radiation. The entire excitation energy may be lost in a single step, as in the case of the decay of Na²² by positron emission (see Fig. VI.7-1). Alternatively, decay to the ground state may take place by emission of gamma rays in several steps (in cascade) until all the excitation energy is lost (see Fig. VI.7-2). In addition, not all the daughter nuclei produced by a given decay lose energy by the same number of steps: some may emit one gamma ray to gain the ground state, while others may emit two or three rays with the same total energy loss (see Fig. VI.7-3). Still other, more complicated decay schemes are known.

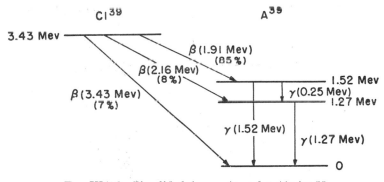

FIG. VI.7-3. *Simplified decay scheme for chlorine*-39.

Nuclear decay schemes such as are illustrated in Figs. VI.7-1 through VI.7-3 are often found or are checked by *coincidence counting*. Nuclear processes generally take place in less than 10⁻¹³ second. Therefore, if it is possible to observe two events connected with the same nuclear process, the fact that they are connected shows as a very precise time coincidence.

The simplest illustration of a coincidence is that of a fast particle traversing two counters and recording in each. If one counter is placed above a cloud chamber and another below, then a time coincidence between the two as recorded by the counters means that a particle has traversed the space between them and therefore also the cloud chamber.

In checking decay schemes it is the time coincidence between gamma radiation and other processes, such as the emission of a beta particle in a nuclear transformation, that is of importance. For example, in the case of a simple decay scheme such as is illustrated in Fig. VI.7-1, the source is mounted between a beta counter and a gamma counter so that disintegrations are recorded in each and the number of coincidences observed. Again, by measurement of neutron coincidences about a fission source, it was shown that, assuming two neutrons per fission, there is a greater likelihood that each fission fragment contributed one neutron than that both neutrons were released from the same fragment.

Coincidence circuits have been used for accurate work on activities of very short half-lives. The source is exposed simultaneously to two counters and the number of times both counters record a disintegration at the same time is determined. Owing to the finite time required for a particle to be recorded (usually of the order of several hundred microseconds for a Geiger-Müller tube) the disintegrations recorded by each of the counters may occur at slightly different times but still be registered as a coincidence. If the time interval within which the two counters record coincidence is variable, the relationship between coincidence rate and resolving time can be determined, from which the half-life of the daughter may be estimated.

Alpha particles may be emitted from a radioactive nucleus in groups of different energies. When a single alpha-particle energy occurs, it is a result of a

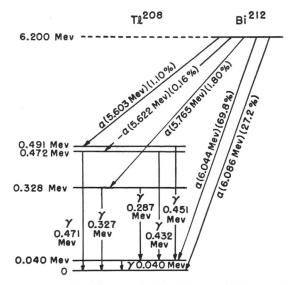

Fig. VI.7-4. *Energy-level diagram for the alpha-particle decay of bismuth-212 to thallium-208.*

transition which takes place between a single energy level of the alpha-emitting nucleus and a single energy level (generally the ground state) of the daughter nucleus. In the majority of cases, the emission of alpha particles in groups of different energies is due to the fact that the daughter can be left in different states of excitation which subsequently transform to the ground state by gamma emission. Each gamma-ray energy observed is, as a rule, equal to the energy difference between the disintegration energies associated with two of the alpha-particle groups. For a complete knowledge of the alpha and gamma energies, an energy-level diagram of the product nucleus (just as for the case of beta emitters) can be constructed (see Fig. VI.7-4).

VI.8. THE TRANSURANIC ELEMENTS

Until a few years ago, the total number of the chemical elements was given as 92. Now these building blocks of nature total 102. Ten new chemical elements have been created and identified. These new elements, occupying a position beyond uranium in the periodic table, are known as the *transuranium*, or *transuranic, elements*.

When Fermi and his group in Rome first exposed uranium to slow neutrons they observed a number of activities. Most of these were assigned to transuranium elements because emissions of beta particles were observed, a process which leads to an increase in the atomic number Z. This assignment seemed to be confirmed by chemical tests which indicated that the new elements had properties different from the elements in the neighborhood of uranium.

In 1939 the discovery of fission led to a new interpretation of the results of the Fermi group. Many of the activities were identified with those belonging to known elements of masses much lower than those of uranium. Further investigation of the fission process (by E. M. McMillan and P. Abelson in 1940) led to the conclusion that one of the observed activities, having a 2.3-day half-life, could not be a product of fission. Actually it was neptunium-239, the daughter of the 23-minute, beta-emitting uranium-239 formed by the $U^{238}(n,\gamma)U^{239}$ reaction. The name neptunium was derived from the planet Neptune, next beyond Uranus.

Neptunium-237 was discovered early in 1942 by bombarding uranium with fast neutrons produced by the Berkeley cyclotron. It was formed as the result of an (n,2n) reaction with uranium-238. Neptunium-237 is of some importance because it has a very long half-life (2.25×10^6 years) as an alpha emitter and it is available in weighable amounts as a result of production in nuclear reactors.

Neptunium-239 emits beta particles, leading to an isotope of element 94, plutonium-239 (named after Pluto, the planet beyond Neptune). Plutonium-239 is an alpha emitter with a half-life of about 2.4×10^4 years. Plutonium-239 was an exciting find because it is fissionable with slow neutrons and is comparatively stable. Careful searches for plutonium in natural ores have shown the presence of extremely small amounts, about 1 part in 10^{14}, in pitchblende and carnotite.

Apparently this plutonium is formed continuously as the result of absorption of neutrons from various sources by the uranium-238 in the ores.

Americium ($Z = 95$) was discovered in 1944. The bombardment of uranium-238 with helium ions of very high energy (40 to 44 Mev) led to the formation of americium-241 as the daughter of the relatively long-lived, beta-emitting plutonium-241 which was primarily produced:

$$U^{238}(\alpha,n)Pu^{241}$$

$$Pu^{241} \rightarrow Am^{241} + \beta^- .$$

Curium ($Z = 96$) was actually discovered in 1944 before the discovery of americium. The first isotope was curium-242 produced by the reaction $Pu^{239}(\alpha,n)Cm^{242}$.

The newest element to be prepared has an atomic number of 102. An international team of scientists claim to have formed an isotope of mass number 253 (with a half-life of 10-12 minutes, decay by alpha particle emission) by bombarding curium-244 with carbon-13 nuclei. A group at the University of California have also prepared element 102 by bombarding curium-246 with carbon-12 or carbon-13. The isotope produced by the latter procedure has a mass number of 254, a half-life of 3 seconds, decaying to fermium-250 ($Z = 100$) by emission of an alpha particle.

VI.9. THERMONUCLEAR REACTIONS

As we have mentioned, when Bohr and Wheeler in 1939 treated the problem of a nucleus in the process of fission theoretically, they thought of their problem in terms of a water droplet undergoing fragmentation from some cause or other. In the same manner, one can approach the nuclear fusion process in terms of two nuclear droplets fusing into a single droplet. With ordinary liquid droplets there is, indeed, a minute release of energy in the fusion process. Whenever there is a disappearance of mass in the process of nuclear fusion, enormous energies are released, analogous to those liberated in the fission process.

In principle, there are many nuclei that can be fused, with an accompanying liberation of energy. However, when one thinks of nuclear fusion, attention is turned to the light nuclei. The reasons for this lie in the charge possessed by each nucleus and the fact that the charges on the two colliding nuclei set up forces of repulsion which oppose the collision. The speed of approach of two nuclei must be great enough to overcome these forces of repulsion if fusion is to occur. Thus two carbon nuclei, of charge +6, would require collision energies of the order of 36 times that necessary to cause deuterium nuclei, charge +1, to fuse.

Thus hydrogen ($Z = 1$), deuterium ($A = 2$), and tritium ($A = 3$) are presently considered the raw materials for fusion processes. Although theoretically and energetically tritium is a more attractive fuel, it is present in water in only infinitesimal quantities or must be produced artificially in nuclear reactions at economically prohibitive costs. On the other hand, deuterium is obtainable in almost unlimited supply from water.

In 1935 Rutherford and Oliphant showed that the reaction

$$_1D^2 + {_1}D^2 \rightarrow {_2}He^3 + {_0}n^1 + 4 \text{ Mev}$$

occurred when solid targets containing deuterium atoms were bombarded with deuterons accelerated to high velocities. Much more energy was expended in the production and through losses of the high-speed deuterons than was obtained by the release of fusion energy. In order to use fusion as a practical source of power, the necessary high velocities of the deuterons will have to be produced by heating a gas to a temperature of millions of degrees instead of by use of an accelerator.

At a few thousand degrees, hydrogen, deuterium, and tritium molecules are completely dissociated into their atoms. At temperatures of the order of 100,000 degrees, the atoms as such no longer exist; there are only nuclei and the stripped-off electrons. To obtain velocities adequate for fusion it is necessary to raise temperatures to the order of hundreds of millions degrees. The practical problem to secure useful energy from fusion, then, is to be able to "heat" materials to this high temperature *and* to provide a container in which the thermonuclear process can be continuously operated *and* to remove the heat at usable temperature ranges.

One place in which the requisite temperature and pressure occurs is in the interior of the sun and other stars. The sun has an internal temperature of about $1.5 \times 10^{6} °C$. The kinetic energy of any nucleus is, then, on the average, about 3000 ev, sufficient to bring two protons together at a separation of about 5×10^{-11} cm. This is not close enough for a direct collision. However, in the irregular heat motion of the nuclei, some move faster and some slower. There will therefore always be a fraction of atoms which happen to have enough speed for a close collision.

According to presently accepted theory, the sun produces fusion energy by an indirect process for the conversion of ordinary hydrogen into helium. This is accomplished by a series of nuclear changes which may be summarized by the following equations:

$$C^{12} + H^1 \rightarrow N^{13} + h\nu \qquad \text{(VI.9-1)}$$

$$N^{13} \rightarrow C^{13} + \beta^+ \qquad \text{(VI.9-2)}$$

$$C^{13} + H^1 \rightarrow N^{14} + h\nu \qquad \text{(VI.9-3)}$$

$$N^{14} + H^1 \rightarrow O^{15} + h\nu \qquad \text{(VI.9-4)}$$

$$O^{15} \rightarrow N^{15} + \beta^+ \qquad \text{(VI.9-5)}$$

$$N^{15} + H^1 \rightarrow C^{12} + He^4. \qquad \text{(VI.9-6)}$$

The overall result is that four protons yield one helium-4 nucleus, two positrons (β^+), and three gamma photons ($h\nu$):

$$4H^1 \rightarrow He^4 + 2\beta^+ + 3h\nu. \tag{VI.9-7}$$

The energy liberated in this reaction is 25.04 Mev. The carbon-12 nucleus acts much like a chemical catalyst for the above series of reactions.

For terrestrial power plants it seems necessary to take the more direct route, say by fusion of deuterium nuclei, requiring temperatures of the order of 10^8 degrees. It is quite evident that, at its temperature of 10^8 degrees, the reaction zone must never be allowed to impinge on the walls of any container; otherwise the latter would be destroyed, or at the very least too much energy would be dissipated, so that the reaction would stop.

One of the present procedures conceives of the reaction zone in the form of a thin circular pencil of heated gas or "plasma" of deuterons and electrons centrally situated in a doughnut-shaped structure capable of maintaining the necessary vacuum conditions, say of the order of 10^{-9} atmosphere. The difficult problems involved are in the production of the necessary temperature for reaction in the plasma of nuclei and electrons and of devices necessary to keep the heated plasma far from the container walls.

One solution of such problems has been supplied by Zeta (the Zero Energy Thermonuclear Assembly) at Harwell, England. This is actually a gas discharge tube of doughnut shape (a torus). The container of the high-temperature zone consists in actuality of magnetic forces created by the discharge itself and by means of an iron core built around the doughnut over part of its length. The toroidal tube is a kind of pulse transformer in which the conducting shell is the primary and the compressed ring of plasma is the secondary. Through this large pulse transformer are passed currents of up to 200,000 amp. The large current inside the torus and passing through the contained deuterium gas not only sets up the discharge in the gas, thereby heating it, but also produces an intense magnetic field around the column of hot gas. Under the influence of the magnetic field the gas discharge becomes even more restricted and, as a consequence, still hotter. The field also causes the discharge to wriggle, and wriggling may bring the hot discharge to the vessel walls. To counteract this and consequent losses in heat, the wriggling is suppressed by applying an additional steady magnetic field parallel to the axis of the tube, supplied by electrical coils fitted around the walls of the tube.

These are the essentials of what is known as the *pinch effect*, the mechanism whereby the electrical discharge as it increases in intensity produces ever stronger magnetic forces sufficient to turn back electrified particles away from the containing walls, compressing them into an ever narrower and more constricted region in the center of the tube. The plasma is confined within this restricted region, which has come to be known as a *magnetic bottle*.

It has been claimed that a temperature of $5 \times 10^{6\circ}$C has been attained with Zeta. Discharges have lasted for 0.004 second. The British have recorded, with reservations, their view that the neutrons produced in Zeta (as well as those produced at Berkeley and Los Alamos) may well have resulted from thermal fusion. It is possible, however, that the neutrons may have been liberated by some other nonthermonuclear mechanism.

VI.10. SYNTHESIS OF THE ELEMENTS

With the relatively simple picture of the structure and interactions of nuclei that are part of present knowledge, many scientists have attempted to explain the origin of the elements by a synthesis starting with the known "fundamental" particles. These efforts have been based primarily on an attempt to deduce the known abundance distribution of the elements as given in the so-called universal or cosmic abundance curve determined by a limited number of observations (see Fig. VI.10-1). The data are derived principally from terrestrial, meteoritic, solar, and other astronomical sources (such as from spectroscopic studies of stellar atmospheres and studies of cosmic radiations). It will be noted in Fig. VI.10-1 that the abundance curve drops rapidly with increasing mass number until about

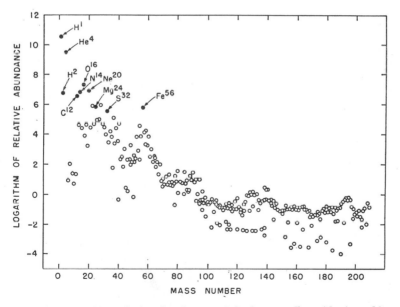

FIG. VI.10-1. *The relative abundances of the isotopes (logarithmic scale) as a function of mass number. This plot was made from the data of H. E. Suess and H. C. Urey,* Rev. Mod. Phys. 28: 53 (1956). *The values were given relative to silicon equal to* 10^6.

$A = 100$. Thereafter, the abundance is relatively constant. A number of superimposed peaks give the curve a very complicated appearance.

It seems possible that all the elements evolved from hydrogen, since the proton is stable and the neutron is not. Moreover, Fig. VI.10-1 shows that hydrogen is the most abundant element; hydrogen atoms constitute about 93 per cent of all atoms by number and 76 per cent by weight. Further, helium, which is the product of hydrogen fusion, is the next most abundant element, being about 7 per cent by number and 23 per cent by weight. All the other elements together constitute only a little more than 1 per cent of the total mass of the universe.

A successful theory of the origin of the nuclei must account for the atomic abundance curve. Some theories have assumed that the elements were built from an unknown and unproved primordial state of the universe, as has been proposed by Gamow and his collaborators. Another theory, due to Hoyle and his co-workers, does not go back quite that far, but proposes that nuclear transformations currently taking place inside of the stars are the source of the heavier elements.

The start is made with hydrogen atoms (or with neutrons that decay into protons and electrons that form hydrogen atoms), existing at this stage in the form of a cold, dilute, but turbulent gas. Part of the turbulent hydrogen gas condenses into stars under the influence of gravitational forces. As the stellar material contracts, the interior becomes dense and very hot from the conversion of gravitational potential energy into thermal kinetic energy. Under these conditions nuclear reactions start, and the star is stabilized as the sources of nuclear energy replace the energy from gravitational contraction. As successive nuclear processes take place, the stars are said to evolve.

When the central temperature of a condensing protostar reaches about $5 \times 10^6 °C$, the protons are in sufficiently rapid relative motion that when two protons collide they can form a deuteron and a positron with the release of energy:

$$_1H^1 + {}_1H^1 \rightarrow {}_1H^2 + \beta^+ + \text{neutrino} + 0.421 \text{ Mev}. \qquad \text{(VI.10-1)}$$

The positron soon annihilates an electron, with the release of additional energy. The deuteron moves about until it reacts with a proton to form helium-3:

$$_1H^2 + {}_1H^1 \rightarrow {}_2He^3. \qquad \text{(VI.10-2)}$$

Helium-3 does not interact with protons. Its concentration can then increase until pairs of such nuclei collide with the production of a helium-4 nucleus and two protons:

$$_2He^3 + {}_2He^3 \rightarrow {}_2He^4 + 2{}_1H^1. \qquad \text{(VI.10-3)}$$

The net effect of this group of reactions is the conversion of four hydrogen atoms into one helium atom, a process called *hydrogen burning*. The result of this is the formation of a core of helium in the star (astrophysical observations indicate that helium mixes with the outer envelope of hydrogen only with extreme difficulty) and this core gradually increases in size as more and more hydrogen is converted. Hydrogen burning is responsible for all of the energy production of stars on the main sequence.

Helium nuclei, because of their double positive charges and therefore greater electric repulsion than is experienced by protons, do not interact at the temperatures at which they were formed from protons. The nuclear proton furnace could go out as a result of the temperature drop (when helium constitutes about 10 per cent of the total stellar mass) were it not for the great gravitational potential energy of the stars. The helium "ash" in the core begins to contract. Again the temperature rises as gravitational energy is converted into kinetic energy.

It might be anticipated that two helium-4 nuclei would interact to form beryllium-8:

$$2_2He^4 \rightarrow Be^8. \hspace{3cm} (VI.10\text{-}4)$$

Inasmuch as no nucleus of mass 8 exists in nature, it may be inferred that it must be unstable. However, the energy of decomposition is relatively small. Artificially produced beryllium-8 has been shown in the laboratory to decay in less than 4×10^{-15} second. If, then, a beryllium-8 nucleus should be formed and if, before it had time to decompose back into two alpha particles, a collision occurred with a third alpha particle, the well-known stable carbon-12 would be formed:

$$3_2He^4 \rightarrow {}_4Be^8 + {}_2He^4 \rightarrow {}_6C^{12} + 7.281 \text{ Mev.} \hspace{1cm} (VI.10\text{-}5)$$

Helium burning takes place at temperatures of about 10^8 degrees and densities of about 10^5 gm/cc; this occurs in the "white dwarf" stars, which therefore represent a late stage of stellar evolution. If the above hypothesis is correct, the chain of element building jumps from helium to carbon, omitting lithium, boron, and beryllium. Justification for the assumption is provided by the observation that these elements are relatively rare in nature; only relatively infrequent secondary processes need be invoked to produce them. Actually it is assumed that they are formed by a spallation process[1] in which protons react with heavy elements.

The production of carbon-12 is followed by a succession of captures of helium nuclei resulting in the formation of oxygen-16, neon-20, and perhaps magnesium-24. The amounts of these isotopes decrease as the Coulomb barrier gets larger. The captures presumably terminate because the helium produced by hydrogen burning becomes exhausted. At this phase there is a further gravitation-induced contraction accompanied by a rise in temperature. At sufficiently high temperatures, probably around $10^9°C$ because of the comparatively large nuclear charges involved, reactions among carbon, oxygen, and neon nuclei occur, leading to the synthesis of the silicon group of elements. Equilibrium will be established at

---

[1] A type of nuclear reaction in which several small particles are ejected from a nucleus; e.g., $Bi^{209} + H^1 \rightarrow Pb^{203} + He^4 + 3n$.

about 5×10^9 degrees. The result, taking place under extreme conditions of temperature and density, will be the formation of the most stable nuclei — iron and the nearby elements. With the production of this group no further release of energy is possible from nuclear processes.

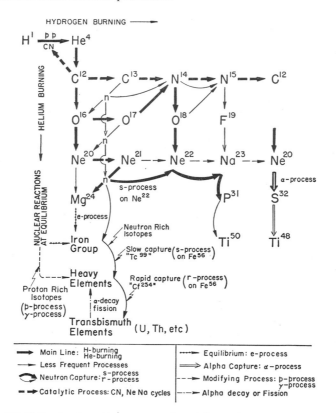

FIG. VI.10-2. *A schematic representation of the nuclear processes by which the syntheses of the elements in the stars occur.* [*Reprinted by permission from E. M. Burbidge et al.,* Rev. Mod. Phys. 29: 547 (1957).]

Hoyle has suggested that the marked peak in the universal abundance curve at the iron group (see mass numbers in the region $A = 50$ to $A = 60$ in Fig. VI.10-1) is due to those stars that remained stable until all nuclear energy release had terminated in the core. Subsequently some had mixed the iron group with the interstellar gas in supernovalike explosions, perhaps induced by sudden mixing of the hot material in the core with the unburned material in the envelope. It has been suggested that stars may even develop shells or layers of successively heavier nuclei: unburned hydrogen on the outside, next helium, then the carbon group, the silicon group, and finally the iron group in the core. Any instability of the star may well lead to the ejection of some or all of this material into space.

Hoyle's suggestion gives an almost exact quantitative description of the relative abundances of titanium, chromium, vanadium, iron, and nickel.

A *second-generation* star will be one that has condensed from hydrogen plus some carbon-12, oxygen-16, neon-20, and even a small amount of the iron in the cosmic gas which results from the explosion of first-generation stars. The hydrogen in the core will be processed into helium not by the mechanism given above but, rather, by other nuclear processes, for example, by the carbon cycle that takes place in the sun (see § VI.9).

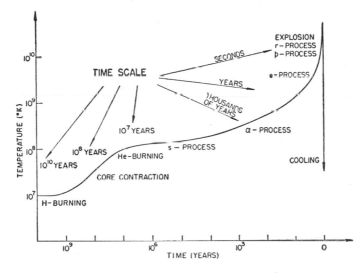

FIG. VI.10-3. *Schematic representation of the time and temperature scales for the various processes of syntheses of elements in the stars.* [Reprinted by permission from E. M. Burbidge et al., Rev. Mod. Phys. 29: 547 (1957).]

The eventual exhaustion of hydrogen will lead to helium burning in the presence of impurities. A second catalytic cycle may also take place in a second-generation star, involving neon-20, neon-21, neon-22, and sodium-23. The nuclei carbon-13, oxygen-17, and neon-21 become very important when the second-generation star exhausts its hydrogen and goes into the red-giant stage. This importance arises from the fact that these three isotopes interact with helium-4 to produce neutrons with a release of energy. These neutrons are readily captured by other nuclei, particularly by those in the iron group, and lead to the formation at reasonable temperatures of the heavy elements up to lead and bismuth. The natural alpha decay of the still heavier nuclei would stop the synthesis at this point. The long-lived parents of the naturally radioactive materials, uranium and thorium, can only be produced in rapid neutron captures. Such might take place in the explosive stages of stellar evolution. Rapid captures will bridge over the alpha-particle activity that circumvents synthesis by capture at a slow rate. Evidence for rapid neutron synthesis became available in the Bikini test in November 1952, when it was found in the thermonuclear debris that californium-254 ($Z = 98$) was produced by rapid neutron irradiation of uranium.

A summary of these processes is given in Fig. VI.10-2. The time scales and temperature of the various processes are summarized schematically in Fig. VI.10-3 for the syntheses of the elements in the star.

Chapter VII

HIGH-ENERGY ACCELERATORS

VII.1. THE VAN DE GRAAFF ELECTROSTATIC GENERATOR

The problem of studying the exceedingly small nucleus is extremely difficult. It is clear that probes of the same order of size as the nucleus itself must be employed to obtain useful information. These probes are, of course, the sub-atomic particles. Clearly, too, positively charged particles must have very high kinetic energies (that is, have very high speeds) if they are to produce inter-actions with nuclei, overcoming the enormous and rapidly increasing forces of repulsion as they approach a nucleus. Thus in the early days of nuclear physics much attention was devoted to the development of methods of accelerating particles such as protons and deuterons.

One of the earliest and, in principle, simplest methods for producing high voltages useful for the acceleration of charged particles is a streamlined version of the familiar electrostatic generator. Van de Graaff was the first to recognize the possibilities of using such a machine to provide high-energy particles for studies in nuclear physics.

In the Van de Graaff machine a high potential is built up and maintained on an insulated conducting sphere by the continuous transfer of electric charges from a moving belt (made of silk, rubber, or other suitable nonconductor) to a metallic sphere (see Fig. VII.1-1). The possibility of constructing such a device is based on the well-known principle that a charge communicated to a spherical metallic conductor is distributed over its surface. A continuous discharge from a high-voltage source (as high as 30 kv has been employed) is maintained at the sharp point A. The positive (or negative) charges are "sprayed" onto the moving flexible belt which carries them into the interior of the insulated metal sphere (sometimes called the corona cap). There another sharp point B connected to the sphere takes off the charges and distributes them to the outside surface of the sphere. The sphere will continue to be charged until the loss of charge from the surface by corona discharge and by leakage along its insulating support balances the rate of charge transfer from the belt.

Since the voltage of an electrostatic generator is limited by the breakdown potential of the gas surrounding the charged electrode, it is desirable to use conditions under which the breakdown potential is as high as possible. The breakdown potential is a function of pressure and goes through a minimum at a small fraction of atmospheric pressure. It is therefore advantageous to operate an electrostatic generator either in a high vacuum (which presents rather formidable practical difficulties) or in a gas at high pressure. Electrostatic generators completely enclosed in steel tanks in which pressures of several atmospheres are

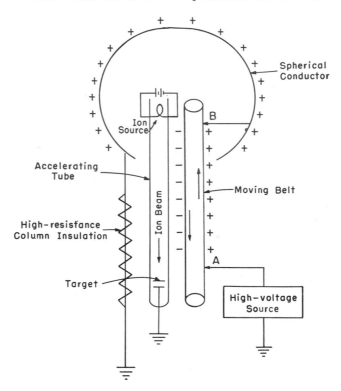

FIG. VII.1-1. *Schematic representation of the Van de Graaff generator.*

used have become common, thereby considerably increasing the potentials obtainable. A further improvement has been the use of gases (such as Freon-nitrogen mixtures) which have high breakdown potentials. Potentials as high as about eight million volts have been developed.

One advantage of the Van de Graaff generator is that ion beams can be produced at voltages which can be maintained constant within about 0.1 per cent or better. Another advantage is that the potential of the sphere can be either positive or negative, so that the particle to be accelerated can be either positive or negative.

The metallic sphere of the Van de Graaff machine is connected to an electrode at one end of the highly evacuated accelerating tube. A target is connected to ground at the other end. The accelerating tube must be sufficiently long to avoid the danger of a spark or other discharge from one end to the other when the potential is applied. The ions are sent through the accelerating tube from a suitable source at the high-potential end to the target at the other end, acquiring increased energy from the electrostatic field as they travel the length of the tube.

VII.2. THE LINEAR ACCELERATOR

Particles accelerated in the Van de Graaff apparatus attain their energy in one step by the application of a high potential. Since this high potential is limited by the breakdown potentials of the insulating materials employed, the velocities imparted to charged particles are limited in value. Higher energies can be obtained by the use of smaller potentials much easier to handle, applied a number of times. This is the basis for the development of the linear accelerator, a name aptly describing the mechanism of operation, which is one of the simplest of machines for the production of accelerated particles.

In the linear accelerator a beam of ions (or electrons) from a suitable source is injected into an accelerating tube containing a number of coaxial, cylindrical sections of increasing length and arranged in a straight line (see Fig. VII.2-1).

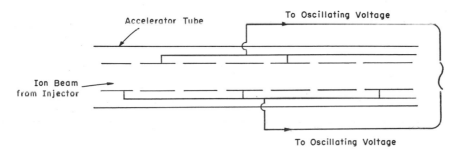

FIG. VII.2-1. *Schematic representation of the accelerator tube of a linear accelerator.*

Alternate sections are connected together electrically, and a high-frequency voltage from an oscillator is applied between the two groups of electrodes. Thus alternate cylinders will carry opposite electric potentials. Inside each metallic cylinder (often called a drift tube), there is a field-free space so that a charged particle, traveling down the tube, will pass through it at a constant speed. The ion will be acted upon only when it is close to or in a gap between the electrodes. The ion gains energy only if the voltage between the electrodes is in the proper phase so that the electric force is in the direction of motion. By correctly choosing (1) the frequency of oscillation of the potential between the two groups of electrodes and (2) the lengths of the successive section, the system can be arranged so that the ions arrive at each gap at the proper phase for a positive acceleration across the gap.

It is evident that the lengths of the successive cylinders must be such that the charged particles spend just one-half cycle of voltage oscillation in each electrode, so that at the time they reach the next gap the potentials are reversed and the ions will receive an additional impulse. Thus if T is the constant time of travel of an ion through any one of the field-free cylinders, L_n the effective length of the n-th cylinder, and v_n the velocity of the ion through it, then

$$T = L_n/v_n. \tag{VII.2-1}$$

Of course, T must also be equal to one-half of the period T_0 of voltage oscillation:

$$T = T_0/2. \tag{VII.2-2}$$

For a constant frequency of voltage oscillation, it is evident that, since the velocity v in each section is increased, the length L of each section must progressively increase if the ions are to be kept exactly in phase with the alternations of the accelerating potential. If V_0 be the average applied potential across each gap, the ion of charge q and mass m will acquire an energy

$$nqV_0 = \tfrac{1}{2}mv_n^2 \tag{VII.2-3}$$

after receiving n impulses. From the above equations

$$L_n = \frac{T_0}{2} \sqrt{\frac{2nqV_0}{m}}, \tag{VII.2-4}$$

so that the length of each cylinder may be correctly calculated.

At very high energies, the velocity of an ion approaches the velocity of light as a limit. Relativistic effects then appear. Each energy increment, then, mainly goes into increasing the mass rather than the velocity. Thus the lengths of the cylinders approach uniformity in size and spacing. By building a sufficiently long system, ions can be made to acquire any desired energy.

VII.3. THE CYCLOTRON

The method for producing positively charged particles of high energy which has attracted the most attention is that employed in the cyclotron. Whereas the principles upon which the electrostatic generator are based can be traced back almost to the beginnings of knowledge about electricity, the cyclotron was based on an entirely new and original idea. E. O. Lawrence of the University of California in 1929 conceived the idea of using magnetic fields to make the particles move in a spiral of increasing radius while being subjected to a large number of comparatively small accelerations, as in the linear accelerator, to increase energy.

The heart of a conventional cyclotron consists of a large, circular vacuum chamber. Inside this are placed two hollow, semicircular metal electrodes, called "dees" because each is shaped like a D. The dees are placed with their straight edges parallel and slightly separated, like a pill box cut in half. From above, the unit looks like a circle (see Fig. VII.3-1). The dees are coupled to a powerful source of radiofrequency voltage supplied by an oscillator. Ions are produced at the center of the chamber between the dees, for example, by fast electrons from an open filament or by an enclosed capillary arc acting on the gas within the

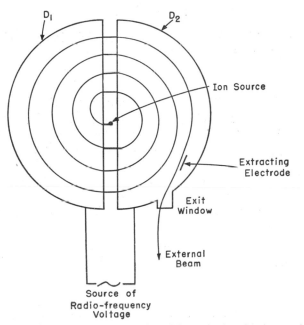

FIG. VII.3-1. *Schematic representation of the path of an ion in a cyclotron.*

chamber. The whole assembly is placed between the pole faces of a large electromagnet to establish a strong magnetic field which makes the charged particles travel in circular orbits.

Assume that, when a positive ion is produced at the source, dee D_1 is at the negative voltage peak of the radiofrequency cycle of potential alteration, and hence that D_2 is at its positive peak. The positively charged ion will be attracted to D_1 and pass into its hollow, field-free interior, acquiring a small velocity. Once inside D_1, the ion is no longer acted on by electrical forces and is unaware of the charge or of a change of charge on D_1; the velocity of the ion will remain constant. However, the magnetic field of the electromagnet does act on the ion, exerting a force on it at right angles to the direction of motion, causing the ion to move in a circular path back to the gap. If, by the time the ion completes a semicircle, the dees have reversed their charge, D_2 now being negative and D_1 positive, the ion will be accelerated across the gap and enter the field-free interior of D_2. The semicircular motion is repeated within D_2, and so on. Every time the ion passes across the gap it gains an increment of kinetic energy equal to its charge ze multiplied by the instantaneous voltage difference (which may be as high as 250 kv) between the dees.

As described for the mass spectrograph (see § I.3) the radius r of the semi-circular path within a dee can be obtained by equating the magnetic force $Hzev$ and the centrifugal force mv^2/r to give

$$r = mv/zeH. \qquad (VII.3\text{-}1)$$

Here H is the magnetic field strength, m the mass of the ion, and v its linear speed. From Equation VII.3-1 it is seen that the greater the velocity of the ion the greater will be the radius of the path. Since the ion gains kinetic energy ($\frac{1}{2}mv^2$) through continued accelerations between the dees, it travels in ever-widening circles until it reaches the exit window at the periphery, where it may be removed from the apparatus by means of a strong electric field applied by the extracting electrode. Assuming that the ions are all formed with the same charge and mass, all the ions would travel along the same path, and have the same velocities and energies.

The striking and significant property of the cyclotron, the quality that makes it a practical success, is that the time taken by the ion to traverse the semi-circular path in the dee is independent of its velocity v or the radius r. In other words, the increase in length of the path is exactly compensated by the increase in the velocity of motion. This may be seen as follows. The length of the semi-circular path is πr. Then the time T taken to traverse the semicircle is

$$T = \pi r/v. \qquad (VII.3\text{-}2)$$

Upon substituting Equation VII.3-1 into VII.3-2, the velocities in numerator and denominator cancel, giving

$$T = \pi m/Hze, \qquad (VII.3\text{-}3)$$

which shows T is independent of both v and r. An ion requires the same time to complete one revolution whether moving near the center of the chamber or close to the periphery. If the radiofrequency ($= \frac{1}{2}T$) of the applied potential is adjusted to the nature of the ion (governed by m and ze) and to the strength (H) of the magnetic field, the ion will always keep in phase with the changes in electric potential between the dees. For magnetic fields of the order of 15,000 gauss, the necessary oscillator frequency as calculated from Equation VII.3-3 in the case of protons turns out to be of the order of 10^7 cycles/second.

From Equation VII.3-1 there is obtained, on squaring and rearranging,

$$\tfrac{1}{2}mv^2 = \frac{(ze)^2H^2}{2m}\,r^2. \qquad (VII.3\text{-}4)$$

Thus, for a given particle and a given magnetic field, the final energy obtainable for a given ion varies with the square of the radius of the cyclotron. Equation VII.3-4 also indicates that the final energy acquired by the ion is entirely independent of the energy increment received at each crossing of the gap between the dees. Further, since the kinetic energy increases as the square of the charge but decreases with the mass, the energy of a beam of alpha particles or protons will be twice that obtainable from deuterons for a given magnetic field; of course, to get this result the radiofrequency oscillation will have to be changed to suit the particle desired. Actually, it is very difficult to change the frequency greatly, so the magnetic field ordinarily is the quantity which is changed to accelerate a different particle. For a constant frequency (variable magnetic field) the attainable kinetic energy is directly proportional to the mass of the particle.

In the equations used above it has been assumed that the mass m of the positive ion remains constant. For energies of the order of 20 Mev this is substantially true, but at higher energies and speeds the relativistic mass effect

$$m = \frac{m_0}{\sqrt{1 - (v^2/c^2)}} \qquad \text{(VII.3-5)}$$

becomes important. From Equation VII.3-3 it can be seen that, as m increases, so will T, the time of transit through a dee. As a result the ion will no longer be in phase with the oscillating potential. Instead of reaching the gap between the dees at the exact instant required for receiving an accelerating impulse, the ions arrive too late and consequently gain little or no additional energy. Thus an approximate limit (about 20 Mev) is set to the energy that can be acquired by an ion in a conventional cyclotron.

VII.4. THE FREQUENCY-MODULATED CYCLOTRON

The relativistic mass effect described at the end of the last section can be compensated by decreasing the frequency of the oscillating potential across the dees of the cyclotron as the mass of the particle increases, while leaving the magnetic field unchanged. Fig. VII.4-1 is a plot of the high-frequency potential as a function of time. In the normal operation of a cyclotron the ion is accelerated at a time, indicated by t_0, just beyond the peak of potential. The ion always arrives at the gap at the appropriate time t_0 to gain its increment of kinetic

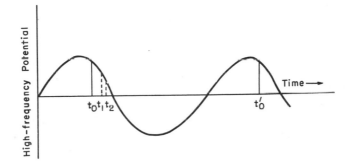

FIG. VII.4-1. *The oscillating potential across the dees of a cyclotron as a function of time.*

energy. With the increase in mass due to relativistic effects as the energy is increased, the ion arrives too late, say at time t_1, so that it will not receive the regular acceleration. Thus a slightly longer time is required for the ion to complete the circle and it will reach the gap gain at a still later time t_2. The voltage kicks progressively become smaller.

E. McMillan in 1945 (and also independently the Russian V. Veksler) proposed a method of compensation by means of a rapidly rotating, variable condenser so that the revolution of the charged particles is automatically synchronized with the changing frequency of the accelerating potential. The name *frequency-modulated cyclotron*, or *synchrocyclotron*, is used for this variation of the cyclotron. In these machines an ion is accelerated to a high energy only if it starts at the right phase of the modulating cycle so that the frequency of the voltage between the dees will decrease in step with the relativistically decreasing frequency of rotation of the particle. The energetic particles are delivered in bursts, one burst for each cycle of modulation, so the average beam current is only about 5 per cent of that in a conventional cyclotron, which gives one burst per cycle of the radio-frequency voltage on the dees. This loss in the number of ions constituting a beam is compensated by the production of ions with much higher energies. Thus the 184-inch California cyclotron can produce deuteron beams of the order of 200 Mev, or alpha particle beams of the order of 400 Mev, using quite moderate dee potentials. The acceleration of particles to these energies has opened up new fields of nuclear research, particularly with respect to the production and study of mesons, hyperons, and antiparticles.

VII.5. THE SYNCHROTRON

Even with the use of frequency modulation, cyclotrons become impractical for the production of energies greater than, say, one billion electron volts (1 Bev). This is principally due to the fact that the cost of the magnets required would be prohibitive. For example, the 184-inch cyclotron at Berkeley contains about 4000 tons of iron in its magnet. Further, in the case of acceleration of electrons (or of any particle whose final speed approaches that of light) the required changes in the frequency of the oscillating potential is beyond practical limits.

From Equation VII.3-3 it is seen that the relativistic effect of increase of mass can be compensated by increasing the magnetic field in an appropriate manner instead of by varying the frequency of oscillation of potential. This is the procedure used in the synchrotron. The magnetic field H is varied in such a manner that the ratio H/m remains constant.

Synchrotrons were originally used for the acceleration of electrons, but machines are now being built for the acceleration of protons. In order to save magnet costs, the charged particles are injected at reasonably high speeds by use of, say, a linear accelerator. Since the initial acceleration is thereby avoided, it is no longer necessary to use the central portions of the cyclotron. Accordingly, the magnetic field need only then fill an annular, or doughnut, region instead of a circular region.

VII.6. THE BETATRON

The cyclotron cannot readily be adapted for use with electrons because of the large relativistic increase of mass at fairly low energies. The Betatron, developed by D. W. Kerst at the University of Illinois to yield 315-Mev electrons, was the first successful apparatus for the multiple acceleration of electrons.

In essence, the basis of operation of the Betatron is the same fundamental principle as that behind the transformer. An electromotive force, causing a current to flow, can be set up in a copper ring enclosing an iron cylinder, providing the latter is increasingly magnetized by the action of a current flowing through a surrounding coil of wire. If the copper ring is replaced by a frictionless tube into which an electron is introduced, the electron undergoes a force which causes its acceleration so long as the magnetic field is increasing. No matter how fast the electron is moving or where it is located, the force will persist if the electron remains at the same radius from the axis of the cylinder. The force on the electron depends on the field strength at the orbit and the rate of change of magnetic flux within the orbit.

In practice the electrons are ejected into an annular vacuum chamber, the "doughnut," from a hot filament and suitably accelerated by an electric field. The injection takes place over a period of 1 to 2 microseconds when the magnetic field in the doughnut is nearly zero. The magnetic field at the doughnut must be such that the electron moves in a circular orbit very close to the centerline of the doughnut. Since (in contrast to the spiral orbit in a cyclotron) the electrons must remain on this circle of fixed radius, the magnetic field at the doughnut must steadily increase as the electrons gain energy as a result of the increasing magnetic flux inside the orbit. Alternatively the orbit may be expanded by sending a pulse of current through a coil to decrease the magnetic field at the orbit. The pole faces are tapered for the purpose of focusing the beam, i.e., to keep the electrons from straying away from the equilibrium orbit.

The rapid variation of the magnetic field necessary for operation of the Betatron is accomplished with a magnet constructed of low-loss laminated iron and energized by an alternating current. Since electrons are injected only once during each cycle of the magnetic field, the time-average electron current obtainable is proportional to the frequency. Frequencies of not more than about 1900 cycles per second have been used, since the cooling of the magnet becomes more difficult with increasing frequency. The time variation of the magnetic field strength in a single cycle of the alternating current is represented in Fig. VII.6-1.

The energy obtainable with a given Betatron is limited by the magnetic saturation in the pole pieces. As the central magnetic flux increases to the point where the iron in the pole pieces begins to saturate, the orbit of the electrons

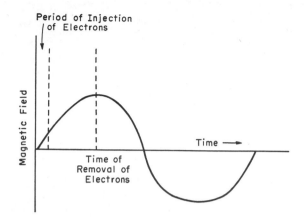

Fig. VII.6-1. *The variation of the magnetic field over a single cycle in the betatron.*

begins to shrink. The electron beam can then be allowed to strike a target mounted in the doughnut inside the equilibrium orbit. For energies above about 300 Mev the Betatron becomes impractical, because with magnets of reasonably small size the energy loss by radiation as the electrons travel in circular paths becomes very serious.

CHAPTER VIII

REACTORS

VIII.1. REACTORS

The fission process, whereby a slow or thermal neutron releases about 200 Mev in inducing the destruction of a uranium-235 nucleus, has been discussed in § VI.5. In order to make this reaction a practical self-sustaining source of nuclear energy, it is evident that a sufficient number of neutrons generated in each fission must induce fission in other uranium nuclei; in fact, it is a minimum requirement that at least one of the neutrons from each fission must cause the further fission of another nucleus. The original neutron acts in this aspect much like a match applied to some combustible material: the heat of the match flame causes a part of the material to burn, and the resulting heat induces combustion of other portions by transfer of energy until the whole is consumed. Inasmuch as an average of 2.47 neutrons are released per uranium-235 fission, it would appear that the requirements can be met.

The problem of producing a nuclear chain reaction by fission would be relatively simple if fission were the only mechanism through which neutrons interact with nuclei, but unfortunately this is not the case. Neutrons can take part in many nonfission reactions, even with uranium nuclei. Neutrons are scattered, both elastically and inelastically, by all kinds of nuclei. In the particular case of uranium-238, neutrons may be captured to form uranium-239. Any other materials present can absorb neutrons. Not all uranium-235 nuclei will undergo fission when they absorb neutrons; actually about 18 per cent of the uranium-236 nuclei formed do not break apart. The uranium-236 nucleus may emit a gamma ray and decay to the ground state, which emits an alpha particle and has a half-life of 2.4×10^7 years. Some cross sections for the different reactions of uranium-235, uranium-238, and natural uranium with thermal neutrons are given in Table VIII.1-1. An additional factor to be considered is that neutrons may be lost from a fissioning system to the outside environment without undergoing reaction.

A problem of extreme importance arises from the fact that the neutrons generated by fission do not have thermal energy, but possess energies up to the order of 10 Mev, the average being about 2 Mev. Although no nuclei have a high probability of capturing high-velocity neutrons, uranium-238 does absorb neutrons at intermediate speeds. There is a certain resonance velocity at an energy in the neighborhood of 5 ev at which uranium-238 has a very large cross section

TABLE VIII.1-1

THERMAL NEUTRON CROSS SECTIONS OF THE
URANIUM ISOTOPES AND NATURAL URANIUM

| | | Cross Section (barns) | |
Reaction	Uranium-235	Uranium-238	Natural Uranium
Fission	582	0	4.18
(n, γ)	112	2.75	3.5
Scattering	9.0	8.3	8.3

for capture. On the other hand, uranium-235, the principal source of fission energy, captures neutrons most readily when they move at thermal velocities, corresponding to an energy of 0.025 ev.

A nuclear reactor is simply an assembly of fissionable material arranged in such a way that a self-sustaining chain reaction is maintained under control. Reactors may be classified in several ways. Thus a thermal reactor is one which utilizes slow or thermal neutrons for the continuation of the fission chain. A fast reactor is one which relies on neutrons of high energy to maintain the chain reaction. The intermediate reactor uses neutrons of intermediate speed. Reactors may also be classified in terms of the nature of the moderator, that is, the particular material which may be used to slow down neutrons from the fast velocities they possess at birth; thus there are water-moderated reactors, heavy-water-moderated reactors, graphite-moderated reactors, and so on. Reactors are sometimes classified according to the nature of the coolant employed in keeping temperatures below dangerous levels. These, then, are light-water-cooled, heavy-water-cooled, gas-cooled, liquid-metal-cooled reactors, etc. Reactors are often classified in terms of the use for which they are intended: power reactors, research reactors, engineering test reactors, and the like. Reactors may be classified according to the fuel which is employed: natural-uranium-fueled, enriched-uranium-fueled, plutonium-fueled, etc.

The underlying principle governing the design, construction and operation of a reactor is based on a conservation or balance of neutrons. As seen above, there are two main processes by which neutrons are lost: (1) by *leakage* from the system, and (2) by absorption, whether this capture result in fission or nonfission. At the same time, neutrons are being *produced* by fission capture in uranium-235 nuclei. Accordingly, the net rate of change of the number of neutrons in the reactor will be equal to the rate at which the neutrons are produced less the rate at which they leak from the system and are absorbed by the materials in the system:

$$\begin{matrix} \text{Rate of change} \\ \text{of neutrons} \end{matrix} = \begin{pmatrix} \text{rate of} \\ \text{production} \end{pmatrix} - \begin{pmatrix} \text{rate of} \\ \text{leakage} \end{pmatrix} - \begin{pmatrix} \text{rate of} \\ \text{absorption} \end{pmatrix}.$$

$$(VIII.1-1)$$

If the system is in an equilibrium state, sometimes called a *steady state*, the rate of change of the number of neutrons will be zero. The equation governing the steady state will then be

$$\text{Rate of production} \atop \text{of neutrons} = \left(\text{rate of leakage} \atop \text{of neutrons}\right) + \left(\text{rate of absorption} \atop \text{of neutrons}\right).$$

(VIII.1-2)

As many neutrons will then be produced by fission as are lost by absorption and leakage.

VIII.2. MODERATION OF NEUTRONS

In reactors which use uranium-235 as a fuel material, thermal neutrons are usually used for the propagation of the nuclear chain reaction. Since the neutrons produced in fission are emitted with average kinetic energies of the order of 2 Mev (fast neutrons), such reactors contain *moderators:* materials whose function it is to slow down (i.e., moderate) the neutrons to thermal energies (0.025 ev) by elastic collisions. The moderating nuclei acquire a portion of the energy of the fast neutron at each collision.

Although it is true that the fast neutrons can cause fission in both uranium-238 and uranium-235, the cross sections, and thus the efficiencies, are much smaller than the cross section for thermal-neutron fission of uranium-235. By slowing down the neutrons before they are absorbed in uranium nuclei, advantage is taken of this larger cross section to increase the probability of sustaining the chain reaction.

It is essential, of course, that a good moderator be a poor absorber of neutrons. In addition, a good moderating material will reduce the speeds of the neutrons in a small number of collisions. This requires that, on the average, there be a considerable decrease of the neutron energy in each collision. In Table VIII.2-1 are given the average number of collisions for several materials which are required to decrease the energy of a 2-Mev neutron to the thermal energy of 0.025 ev.

TABLE VIII.2-1

MODERATOR PROPERTIES

Element	Mass Number	*Calculated Collisions Required for Thermalization*
H	1	18
D	2	25
He	4	43
Li	7	67
Be	9	86
C	12	114
O	16	150
U	238	2172

A thermal reactor will thus consist of a mass of fissionable material distributed throughout a moderating material. The choice of moderator is partly dependent on the composition of the fuel. For example, ordinary water cannot be used as a moderator if natural uranium is employed, because the hydrogen in the water can capture neutrons to an appreciable extent.

For a given scattering angle, the fractional decrease in the kinetic energy of a neutron involved in an elastic collision is greater the more closely the mass of the scattering nucleus approaches that of the neutron, for the same reason that when a billiard ball hits an object more massive than itself it rebounds with little loss of speed. This is borne out by the data given in Table VIII.2-1. It will be obvious that a good moderator will consist of atoms of low mass number, because the neutron has a mass only slightly larger than that of a hydrogen atom.

The size of the reactor will depend to some extent on the nature of the moderator employed. In a reactor using a good moderator, such as light water, the fuel elements may be packed quite closely together, since not so many collisions are required to slow down the neutrons before they encounter fissionable nuclei. With heavy water, the number of collisions required to thermalize the neutrons is larger; therefore the neutrons must traverse greater distances before acquiring thermal energies, so that the fuel elements must be placed farther apart.

In order that the thermalization process may take place as rapidly as possible, a solid or a liquid moderator is employed. The energy-reducing collisions will occur more frequently when the packing of the atoms is closer than in the gaseous state.

Hydrogen-containing materials would seem to be ideal to serve as moderators because the mass of the hydrogen atom is close to that of the neutron. Unfortunately, hydrogen nuclei have a comparatively large cross section for the capture of neutrons as a result of the reaction

$$_1H^1 + {_0}n^1 \rightarrow {_1}H^2 + h\nu. \tag{VIII.2-1}$$

Heavy water (D_2O) is better than ordinary water (H_2O) as a moderator because the capture of neutrons by deuterium nuclei is much less than by an equal number of hydrogen nuclei, although the energy decrease per collision is larger for hydrogen than for deuterium. On the other hand, if the increased absorption of neutrons is not critical to the operation of a reactor, ordinary water is attractive because of its low cost. Ordinary water is thus quite useful for reactors such as might be found in submarines, for only a few collisions would be required to produce slow neutrons.

Although many more collisions are required to slow down neutrons by a graphite moderator than by either hydrogen or deuterium, graphite has been widely employed for moderating purposes because of its extremely small capture cross section for neutrons. In a collision with a carbon nucleus, a neutron will lose about one-sixth of its energy per collision. Other substances of lower atomic weight that may be used include beryllium and lithium-7.

Fast reactors do not require the use of a moderator.

VIII.3. THE FUEL

The fuel element of a reactor contains fissionable material. It may be built in many different shapes; a long cylindrical rod, a tube, a plate, and so on.

One of the first steps in the design of a reactor is to decide on the fuel material. Metallic uranium may be used. It has the disadvantages, however, of being quite reactive chemically, of undergoing phase changes at high temperature, and of deforming as a result of radiation damage. Some of these disadvantages can be partially eliminated by alloying with other metals. If operation at low temperatures is anticipated, aluminum may be employed. If the design of the reactor requires the use of materials which do not have high cross sections for the absorption of neutrons, zirconium may be used as the alloying material. If the reactor is to operate at high temperatures, stainless steel can be utilized with the uranium as an oxide dispersed in the steel.

A chain reaction can be maintained with uranium dioxide (UO_2), because oxygen is a poor absorber of neutrons; of course, the compound must be exceedingly pure.[1] From the nuclear point of view the use of the oxide is not as good as the use of the metal, but the former does have the advantage of being able to withstand higher temperatures and greater fuel burnups.

In general the fuel is clad with some corrosion-resistant material. This protects the fuel element from corrosion with its attendant radioactive contamination of the coolant; in such an event there could be a serious biological hazard to personnel. The cladding also serves to prevent escape of the radioactive fission products, including gases. Aluminum has been extensively used as a cladding material; for operations at higher temperatures, zirconium or stainless steel may be employed.

The use of cladding introduces many problems for the reactor designer. For example, the temperature in the fuel element is higher than in surrounding regions because of the energy released in fission. In order to prevent the temperature from becoming too high and ruining the fuel element, heat must be conducted away. Accordingly there must be a good bond between the cladding and the uranium to allow for the heat conduction. In addition, the cladding must have suitable mechanical properties to withstand thermal stresses and dimensional changes because of radiation damage of the fuel.

In the choice of fuel it must be considered that both uranium-235 and uranium-238 compete for neutrons. The competition by uranium-238 is important because of its much greater abundance (about 140 times that of uranium-235, as shown in Table VIII.3-1) and because, as mentioned in § VIII.1, the uranium-238 is more likely to absorb neutrons at intermediate speeds than are nuclei of uranium-235. One way to get around this difficulty would be to get rid of the uranium-238 and use almost pure uranium-235, such as is used in some types of

[1] The world's first reactor utilized both uranium and uranium oxide (U_3O_8); only a small amount of sufficiently pure uranium was available when it was constructed.

TABLE VIII.3-1

PERCENTAGE ABUNDANCES OF THE URANIUM ISOTOPES

Mass of Isotope	Natural Abundance, per cent
234	0.006
235	0.714
238	99.280

atomic bombs. The separation of uranium-235, however, is costly. Natural uranium may be used if the fast neutrons produced by fission are slowed down quickly to arrive at thermal speed, favored by uranium-235, instead of being absorbed by uranium-238. This is the function of the moderator (see § VIII.2) in a reactor.

In the original, "pile type" of reactor (so called because it had the shape of a large block built up as a lattice of uranium and graphite) thin rods of pure natural uranium, about an inch in diameter and encased in aluminum (a weak absorber of neutrons) to prevent oxidation, were inserted into blocks of graphite. The fast neutrons produced by fission in such a rod escaped from the rod into the graphite. By the time the neutrons passed through this moderator, their speeds had been reduced to values which favored capture by uranium-235 rather than by uranium-238.

The fuel rods may be arranged in clusters. Such an assembly presents a greater surface to the coolant and simplifies the problem of heat removal.

If uranium-235 were the only fissionable material, there would be little hope for economical nuclear power plants. The isotope is too rare to be considered seriously as a fuel for economical, large-scale use. Much of the hope for practical economic nuclear power lies in the fact that it is possible to manufacture two other fissionable materials: plutonium and uranium-233.

Plutonium is produced by the following series of reactions:

$$U^{238} + n^1 \rightarrow U^{239}$$

$$U^{239} \xrightarrow{\text{23 min}} Np^{239} + \beta^-$$

$$Np^{239} \xrightarrow{\text{2.3 days}} Pu^{239} + \beta^-.$$

The manufacture of uranium-233 is based on the following sequence:

$$Th^{232} + n^1 \rightarrow Th^{233}$$

$$Th^{233} \xrightarrow{\text{23 min}} Pa^{233} + \beta^-$$

$$Pa^{233} \xrightarrow{\text{27 days}} U^{233} + \beta^-.$$

Both sets of reactions depend at present on the fission of uranium-235 as the source of neutrons.

A reactor using natural uranium is deliberately designed to make most of the neutrons bypass the absorption by uranium-238 in order to maintain the chain reaction. But some neutrons are inevitably absorbed by some of the uranium-238. Thus even in a reactor running at a very low power level, a little plutonium is created in the uranium. To increase the production of plutonium, the power level is raised. This is the basis of operation of the plutonium-producing reactors at Hanford. Periodically the uranium rods are removed and the plutonium is extracted by chemical methods.

VIII.4. COOLANTS

Since most of the energy liberated in fission ultimately appears as heat, a nuclear reactor must have an adequate cooling system which will prevent the temperature from reaching undesirable and damaging levels. In general, cooling is done by circulating a heat-transfer medium, called the coolant, through the reactor and then through a heat exchanger in which steam may be produced.

Overheating may cause warping of the fuel elements, melting, or other damage to the reactor (see Fig. VIII.4-1). The coolant employed, whether gaseous or liquid, must be able to withstand high temperatures and the actions of the nuclear radiations. If the coolant nuclei capture neutrons, a radioactive product may be formed. In a power reactor, for example, this is an operating difficulty because the fluid circulates between the reactor and the heat exchanger; the power equipment may become contaminated with radioactive materials and dangerous to operating personnel. In addition, a coolant should have a high boiling temperature, if liquid, and be efficient for the transfer of heat. In any event, the specific requirements will depend largely upon the rate at which heat is produced.

Water has been widely used as a coolant (because of its low cost, availability, and familiar technology) although it has a number of disadvantages: comparatively large cross section for the capture

Fig. VIII.4-1. *Damage sustained by the core of the EBR-I as a result of too high a temperature.*

of neutrons, decomposition caused by the nuclear radiations, corrosive action upon metals, and relatively low boiling point at normal pressures. In order to make the attainment of high operating temperatures possible, water is used under pressure, so as to raise its boiling point. The use of water as a coolant generally requires an increased (and expensive) loading of fuel in order to compensate for the loss of neutrons by capture.

The most suitable gaseous coolants appear to be helium and carbon dioxide. Air, which might be an obvious choice, is not a good heat-transfer material; in addition, both oxygen and nitrogen may be corrosive to the reactor constituents at high operating temperatures. Helium has some advantages over carbon dioxide as a coolant, because of its rate of heat transfer and because its capture cross section for neutrons is virtually zero. Carbon dioxide is, of course, more readily available and much cheaper. In order to increase the density, high pressures must be used. The British are using carbon dioxide in their Calder Hall development, and the AEC has started a program of investigating the usefulness of gaseous coolants in reactors.

Organic liquids, which have been suggested as reactor coolants, decompose at high temperatures. They are also subject to decomposition as a result of the actions of neutrons, beta, and gamma radiations.

Liquid metals offer good prospects as coolants because of their stability at high temperatures and their good heat-transfer properties. In addition, since their vapor pressures are low at high temperatures, high-pressure equipment is not necessary. These characteristics are of special importance in fast reactors. Mercury, the only liquid metal at room temperature, has too high a capture cross section. Materials such as sodium or sodium-potassium alloy (NaK) appear to be very promising liquid metal coolants, however, particularly at the high temperatures encountered in fast reactors. The NaK alloy has the advantage over sodium of being liquid at room temperature, but it has a higher cross section for absorption of neutrons. Another disadvantage, mainly because of the great chemical reactivity, is that their use requires extremely special and expensive handling equipment.

In power reactors, as has been mentioned, the coolant is heated by the fuel and then passes to a heat exchanger. Here the heat may be used indirectly to run a turbine and thereby generate electricity. The power attainable will be limited by the ability of the coolant to remove heat.

VIII.5. REACTOR OPERATION

If a reactor were infinite in size, there would be no leakage of neutrons (either fast or slow) from it. The steady-state equation (VIII.1-2) would then simply reduce to:

Rate of production of neutrons = rate of absorption of neutrons.   (VIII.5-1)

In actual practice, however, neutron leakage does occur; but the proportion of neutrons thus lost by escape from a reactor of finite size can be diminished by increasing the size of the system. The escape of neutrons by leakage from the reactor occurs at the exterior surface; thus the number of neutrons lost in this fashion depends on the external surface area. For a reactor of a given size, then, the amount of leakage, other factors being constant, will be dependent upon the shape; it may be anticipated that a spherical reactor, having the smallest surface area for a given volume, will have the smallest leakage. A cube will be nearly as good.

The absorption of neutrons leading to fission, and thereby to the production of neutrons required to sustain the chain reaction, occurs throughout the fuel. In other words, the number of neutrons formed will be a function of the volume. (The same is true, of course, for absorption leading to nonfission reactions.) The volume of a reactor increases at a more rapid rate than does the surface area. Hence the relative loss of leakage of neutrons can be reduced by increasing the volume, and hence the mass, of the reactive material. This basic geometrical law is one of the principal factors in the design of reactors.

The *critical size* of a reactor is defined as that size at which neutrons are produced at a sufficient rate to keep the reaction self-sustaining despite the loss of neutrons by leakage and nonfission captures. Fission will then continue at a constant rate. Equation VIII.1-2 will hold. If a reactor is smaller than the critical size, neutrons are lost at a greater rate than they are replenished by fission, and a self-sustaining chain reaction is impossible.

The critical size is not a constant. It depends upon a great many factors: the nature of the materials used in the reactor, the isotopic composition of the uranium, the geometry of the assembly, the accumulation of neutron absorbers among the fission products, and so forth.

The critical size or mass of a reactor can be reduced to an appreciable extent by surrounding the core of the reactor with a scattering material called a *reflector*. This scatters a portion of the neutrons that would otherwise leak, back into the reactor proper where they can be used to advantage, particularly in utilizing the fuel near the reactor boundaries. The use of a reflector, which is often of the same material as the moderator, permits a considerable saving in the amount of fissionable material needed. In addition, the average power output of a reactor for a given weight of fuel is increased.

In order to maintain a chain reaction it is not necessary that every neutron produced in fission should be able to initiate another fission. The required condition is that for each nucleus undergoing fission there shall be produced, on the average, at least one neutron that causes fission of another nucleus. This is precisely the condition in a reactor of the critical size. The neutron density will then remain constant.

The ratio of the number of neutrons in one generation to that in the immediately preceding generation is called the *effective multiplication constant k*. In terms of this definition, it is seen that

$$k = \frac{\text{new neutrons}}{\text{neutrons lost}} \qquad \qquad \text{(VIII.5-2)}$$

$$= \frac{\text{number of neutrons created}}{\text{number of neutrons leaking} + \text{number of neutrons absorbed}}.$$

In the reactor of critical size, as may be seen by comparison with Equation VIII.1-2, $k = 1$. If k is less than unity, even by a very small amount, the chain reaction cannot be maintained, for neutrons will be lost at a greater rate than they are replenished by fission. The reactor will shut itself down. If k is greater than unity, the numerator in Equation VIII.5-2 is larger than the denominator, and the neutron population increases continually. Such a reactor is said to be divergent. Larger and larger amounts of energy will be liberated. If this condition is permitted to continue, the results can be catastrophic in the sense that the reactor is severely damaged, but not in the sense of an explosion such as is produced by a nuclear bomb. Reactor designs are such that a nuclear explosion cannot take place.

It is seen that the desired condition for reactor operation is that $k = 1$. In practice, however, reactors are designed in such a way that k *can* be made slightly larger than 1. (Too large an excess makes reactor control more difficult.) One of the reasons for this is that a reactor run at a high level of power quickly becomes poisoned by its own fission products. Some of these are very avid absorbers of neutrons. As they are formed, k decreases, since more neutrons would be absorbed in nonfission reactions. The reactor would shut itself down even though only a small portion of the fissionable material had been used. By building the reactor in such a way that k can be made greater than unity, refueling occurs less often. Then, by means of *control rods*, the reactor can be made supercritical ($k > 1$), just critical ($k = 1$), or subcritical ($k < 1$). All three conditions are needed.

The control rods are made of materials, such as cadmium or boron-containing steel, which have large cross sections for the absorption of neutrons. The control rods are introduced into the reactor to accurately adjustable depths. The deeper the penetration of the control rods into the reactor, the greater will be the number of neutrons absorbed by them and the smaller will k become. When the reactor has reached a predetermined power level, the control rods serve to keep, through adjustment of their positions and thereby of the number of neutrons absorbed, the effective multiplication factor at unity.

In order to increase the power and neutron density of a reactor, k must be made greater than 1. This can be done by partially removing the control rods. The multiplication factor exceeds unity and the neutron density rises. When this attains the desired value, the control rods are inserted to the extent necessary to again keep the power constant.

When a reactor is to be shut down, the control rods are inserted to a considerable depth. So many neutrons are then captured by them that k becomes less than 1 and the chain reaction can no longer be maintained.

To start a reactor the control rods are partially withdrawn. The chain reaction then develops rapidly. Fortunately, because of the delayed neutrons (see § VI.5), the system has enough inertia so that an operator has ample time to bring the controls into play as the chain reaction increases.

Increases in power level normally result in increases of temperature. This produces reductions in the densities of fuel, moderator, and coolant. The density changes result in increase rates of leakage of neutrons from the reactor, producing a leveling of the power. In other words, the reactors are partially self-leveling with respect to power levels; that is, reactors have negative power temperature coefficients. Higher temperatures have several other minor effects that tend to reduce the power levels of reactors.

VIII.6. REACTOR POWER

The total energy release in each fission is about

$$200 \text{ Mev} = 3.2 \times 10^{-4} \text{ erg}$$

$$= 3.2 \times 10^{-11} \text{ watt-sec.}$$

Thus in a reactor operating at a power of 1 watt, about 3×10^{10} fissions take place every second. A reactor generating 1 megawatt of power will thus utilize about 1 gm of uranium per day. This may be calculated as follows. There are $(60 \text{ sec/min})(60 \text{ min/hr})(24 \text{ hr/day}) = 8.6 \times 10^4 \text{ sec/day}$. For operation at 1 watt per day, the rate of fission of uranium will be $(8.6 \times 10^4 \text{ sec/day})(3 \times 10^{10}$ fissions/sec$) = 2.6 \times 10^{15}$ fissions/day. For operation at 1 megawatt $(= 10^6$ watts) per day, 2.6×10^{21} fissions will be required. Since 235 grams of uranium-235 contain 6×10^{23} atoms, then 6×10^{23} atoms/235 gm U-235 $= 2.5 \times 10^{21}$ atoms/gm uranium-235. Thus the 2.6×10^{21} fissions required will correspond to slightly more than 1 gm of uranium-235.

Suppose that a reactor in operation provides a neutron density of n neutrons per cubic centimeter and that each neutron moves, on the average, with a speed of v cm/sec. The product nv (which thus has the dimensions of neutrons per square centimeter per second) is called the *neutron flux* and is generally denoted by the symbol ϕ:

$$\phi = nv. \tag{VIII.6-1}$$

In effect the neutron flux may be represented simply as the sum of the distances traveled in 1 second by all the neutrons contained in 1 cubic centimeter. Suppose N represents the number of fissionable nuclei (say, of uranium-235) per cubic centimeter and that V is the volume (in cubic centimeters) of the reactor.

Then the total number of fissionable nuclei available to the n neutrons will be NV. If σ_f denote the cross section of uranium-235 for fission, then $\sigma_f NV$ is the effective area in the reactor for fission. Thus the total number of nuclei A undergoing fission per second in the reactor is given by

$$A = nvNV\sigma_f. \qquad \text{(VIII.6-2)}$$

If 3.1×10^{10} fissions are required per second to produce 1 watt of power, then the power P of the reactor is given by

$$P = \frac{nvNV\sigma_f}{3.1 \times 10^{10}} \qquad \text{(in watts)}$$

$$= \frac{nvNV\sigma_f}{3.1 \times 10^{16}} \qquad \text{(in megawatts).} \qquad \text{(VIII.6-3)}$$

For a given reactor, N, V, and σ_f may be regarded as essentially constant. Accordingly, the power of that reactor will be proportional to the average neutron flux φ. If the average speed of the neutrons is assumed to be approximately constant, then the power will vary as the mean neutron density n. (Actually, there exists a distribution of velocities for the neutrons in a reactor.)

VIII.7. STRUCTURAL MATERIALS

The materials used in the construction of reactors are at present subject to much more stringent requirements than are those employed in conventional types of power plants. To approach any reasonable efficiency in the extraction of nuclear energy from a reactor it is required that operation be at reasonably high temperature. Unfortunately, materials are very susceptible to damage by heat; most practical materials will not tolerate temperatures as high as 1000°C. Thus there exists a relatively low upper limit of attainable temperatures for practical operation of stationary power plants. Reactor designers have to consider the effects of heat on all the components: fuel, moderator, coolant, controls, reflectors, pipes, etc.

In addition to possessing great strength, resistance to deformation under stresses, and ability to withstand high temperatures, materials that are used in the cores or fuel sections of reactors must not capture neutrons to any great extent. This requirement means not only the use of special materials, but also that such materials may have to be of very high purity to avoid loss of neutrons. Another restriction upon materials used in reactors is that they must have the ability to withstand the continuous destructive bombardment of the various nuclear radiations produced in the reactor. Such radiations can change the internal structure of solids, even of uranium itself, thereby possibly seriously affecting their physical and mechanical properties. An important example is given by the (n,γ) reactions, which often produce radioactive isotopes of the materials used. Materials that withstand the effects of the radiations do not necessarily tolerate high temperatures. In addition, the rates of corrosion of materials may be enhanced by the action of the radiations.

The number of metals with small cross sections for the absorption of thermal neutrons is very limited. These are beryllium, magnesium, zirconium, and aluminum. Aluminum has been used extensively where exposure to high temperatures is not involved. Magnesium is much less corrosion-resistant than aluminum, and beryllium is expensive and very difficult to fabricate into tubes and to weld. Zirconium has become a prominent structural material for use in reactors, particularly where water at high pressures and moderate temperatures is used as a coolant. The metal, which has not been available in commercial

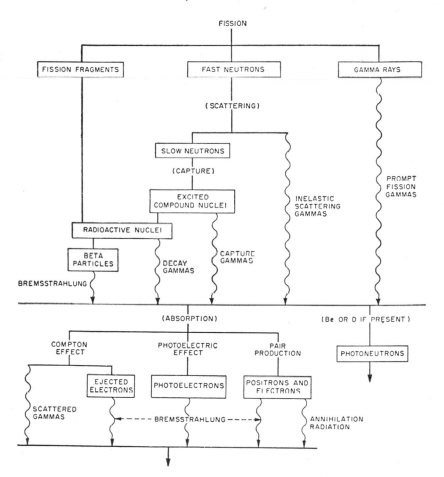

Fig. VIII.8-1. *Radiations from a nuclear reactor.* [*Reprinted by permission of the U. S. Atomic Energy Commission from S. Glasstone,* Principles of Nuclear Reactor Engineering, *D. Van Nostrand Co., Inc., Princeton, N. J.,* (1955), *p. 578.*]

quantities of reasonable purity until recently, has excellent mechanical and reasonable fabrication properties, and is fairly resistant to corrosion up to 300°C.

VIII.8. SHIELDING

A reactor is an intense source of nuclear radiations arising from the fission process, the various radioactive decays of the fission fragments, and secondary processes. The complex character of the nuclear radiations is illustrated in Fig. VIII.8-1.

Any alpha and beta particles produced are easily stopped; but the absorption of neutrons and gamma rays is a much more difficult matter because of their considerable penetrating power. By means of shielding, these must be reduced to levels outside the reactor at which people, instruments, and equipment can function properly.

The best absorbers for gamma radiation, both primary and secondary, are materials of high density, such as lead. Because of cost, however, lead is not extensively used to shield reactors. Iron is a reasonable compromise between cost and high-density considerations.

Since the cross sections for capture of neutrons are generally larger for slow than for fast neutrons (the $1/v$ law), shielding from neutrons is generally based on decreasing their speed and then absorbing them in a suitable material. As seen in § VIII.2, the best moderators for slowing down neutrons are elements of low mass number. In this respect, hydrogen seems to be eminently suitable, for it not only slows neutrons but absorbs them. Liquid water is suitable as a shielding material for neutrons, but has a low density and a poor absorption for gamma rays. Accordingly, concrete, which contains a large proportion of hydrogen as either free or combined water, has been widely used. It is cheap and easy to install.

Unfortunately, concrete alone does not provide a complete solution to the problem of neutron shielding. Gamma radiation of 2.21-Mev energy is liberated by the $H^1(n,\gamma)H^2$ reaction. These gamma rays must be absorbed. Since, as mentioned above, iron is a suitable material for gamma-ray absorption, special concretes have been made which use a considerable proportion of an iron oxide ore. Small pieces of metallic iron, such as steel punchings, may also be included. In addition, iron has an appreciable cross section for the capture of thermal neutrons. Boron in various forms may be added to the concrete in order to increase the neutron absorption.

In essence, then, a reactor shield may contain elements of high mass number to absorb gamma radiation, elements of low mass number to thermalize neutrons, and a good neutron absorber.

Another factor that must be taken into consideration is that all the energy absorbed in the shield is ultimately degraded into heat. Since the absorption of both gamma rays and neutrons is approximately exponential in nature, much of this heat appears in regions close to the core. To protect the shield from possible heat damage, a so-called *thermal shield*, as contrasted with the *biological shield*, is frequently placed close to the reactor proper. It consists of a substantial thickness of a dense metal of fairly high melting point, such as steel.

VIII.9. BREEDING

Uranium-235 is the isotope of uranium in which fission occurs most readily. Unfortunately, it is present in natural uranium to the extent of only 1 part in about 140. The situation is saved by the fact that the absorption of neutrons in the more plentiful uranium-238 leads to fast fission or to the production of fissionable plutonium-239. Thorium-232, too, may be converted into fissionable uranium-233.

The number of new fissionable atoms formed per atom of fuel destroyed is called the *conversion ratio*. Conversion ratios in thermal reactors vary from zero in reactors employing uranium-235 as the fuel to nearly 1.0 for reactors containing thorium and burning uranium-233. Production reactors with natural uranium serving as fuel have conversion ratios between 0.8 and 1.0. Thermal power reactors which employ slightly enriched uranium have conversion ratios of 0.6 to 0.85.

It is possible to design a reactor, called a *breeder*, in which more fissionable material is formed in each generation than is used up in fission. If, for every uranium-235 nucleus undergoing fission, one neutron served to carry on the reaction chain and one neutron (out of the average 2.5 produced per fission) were captured by uranium-238 to produce plutonium, there would be no loss of fissionable material. If more than one neutron were used for the production of plutonium, the stockpile of fissionable material could be steadily increased, instead of remaining constant as would be the case for the one-to-one conversion. With breeding, all the uranium (as well as thorium) could ultimately be utilized, instead of just the uranium-235 isotope. To accomplish this, special precautions have to be taken to avoid the loss of neutrons by leakage and by capture in materials other than uranium. The prevention of such losses is not an easy matter. Moreover, the requirements for a power reactor — high operating level, coolant system, and so on — tend to increase the loss of neutrons.

The relative losses of neutrons are least in a reactor operating on fast neutrons rather than on thermal neutrons, for there is no absorption in a moderator or materials of construction. In addition, no element has strong capture resonances for fast neutrons. This gives fast reactors a higher probability for success as breeders. When plutonium is used as a fuel, a conversion ratio of 1.7 is possible.

In the construction of a breeder reactor, the fertile material (uranium-238 to produce plutonium-239, or thorium-232 to produce uranium-233) may be made part of the fuel unit itself, or it may form a "blanket" or reflecting shield surrounding the core of fuel. In either case the manufactured fissionable material must be separated from the parent fertile material. Such a chemical separation is readily carried out very efficiently. Unless this is done, the whole of the breeding process might be futile, since more fissionable material might thereby be lost than would be gained by the breeding.

Chapter IX

METALLURGY OF URANIUM

IX.1. THE OCCURRENCE OF URANIUM

Uranium is the basic source material of nuclear energy by fission. As found in nature, uranium has the following isotopic composition:

ISOTOPE	NATURAL ABUNDANCE (%)
238	99.3
235	0.7
234	Trace

According to geologists, uranium is present to the extent of 3 to 4 parts per million in the crust of the earth. This represents an abundance about the same as that of zinc, lead, and tin, and much greater than that of mercury, silver, and gold. Unfortunately, uranium does not often occur in highly concentrated deposits.

The largest deposits of minerals relatively rich in uranium were situated in the Great Bear Lake area of Canada primarily as pitchblende, and in the Belgian Congo in Africa. The highest grade ores have been pretty much exhausted. In the United States uranium has been found in economically extractable deposits principally in Colorado, Utah, Arizona, and New Mexico. The principal uranium minerals found in the United States are listed in Table IX.1-1. In them uranium occurs in the tetravalent or the hexavalent state.

TABLE IX.1-1

PRINCIPAL URANIUM MINERALS OF THE UNITED STATES

Mineral	Composition
Uraninite	uranium oxide — $x\mathrm{UO}_2 \cdot y\mathrm{UO}_3$
Pitchblende	uranium oxide — $x\mathrm{UO}_2 \cdot y\mathrm{UO}_3$
Coffinite	uranium silicate — $\mathrm{U(SiO_4)}_{1-x}\mathrm{(OH)}_{4x}$
Carnotite	potassium uranium vanadate — $\mathrm{K_2O} \cdot 2\mathrm{UO}_3 \cdot \mathrm{V_2O_5} \cdot 3\mathrm{H_2O}$
Tyuyamunite	calcium uranium vanadate — $\mathrm{CaO} \cdot 2\mathrm{UO}_3 \cdot \mathrm{V_2O_5} \cdot 8\mathrm{H_2O}$
Torbernite	copper uranium phosphate — $\mathrm{CuO} \cdot 2\mathrm{UO}_3 \cdot \mathrm{P_2O_5} \cdot 8\mathrm{H_2O}$
Autunite	calcium uranium phosphate — $\mathrm{CaO} \cdot 2\mathrm{UO}_3 \cdot \mathrm{P_2O_5} \cdot 8\mathrm{H_2O}$
Uranophane	calcium uranium silicate — $\mathrm{CaO} \cdot 2\mathrm{UO}_3 \cdot 2\mathrm{SiO_2} \cdot 6\mathrm{H_2O}$
Schroeckingerite	hydrated uranium carbonate of calcium — $3\mathrm{CaO} \cdot \mathrm{Na_2O} \cdot \mathrm{UO_3} \cdot \mathrm{CO_2} \cdot \mathrm{SO_3F} \cdot 10\mathrm{H_2O}$

IX.2. THE PREPARATION OF URANIUM

The principal stages in the processing of uranium ores to obtain the metal are:

(1) Concentration of the ore
(2) Preparation of orange uranium oxide (UO_3)
(3) Conversion of the orange oxide to green salt (UF_4)
(4) Reduction of green salt to the metal

Although there are many types of minerals which contain uranium, all chemical processing methods involve digestion with either acid or alkaline reagents. The choice depends on the type of ore. In acid processes, sulfuric acid is most often used. If the uranium in the ore is in the tetravalent state, oxidizing agents (such as manganese dioxide or chlorine) may be employed to produce the more soluble hexavalent UO_2SO_4, which occurs in solution in the form of several anion complexes. In alkaline processes, sodium carbonate or sodium bicarbonate are widely used, leading to the soluble complex uranyl carbonate anion $UO_2(CO_3)_3^{-4}$; again, oxidants may be employed to raise the valence of the uranium from 4 to 6.

For the concentration of the uranium, various methods have been used: precipitation, partial reduction followed by precipitation, electrolysis, ion exchange procedures, and solvent extraction. The uranium can be quantitatively precipitated from suitably prepared ore solutions by using an alkali or hydrogen peroxide. Both of these reagents have disadvantages, so that frequently the hexavalent uranium is reduced to the tetravalent state before precipitation with fluoride or phosphate ion. Removal of the uranium by electrolysis has been especially useful in dealing with carbonate solutions. Amberlite IRA-400, among others, has been found satisfactory as an anion exchange resin to concentrate the uranium from either the sulfuric acid or the carbonate leaches, especially when the solutions are very dilute.

The orange oxide is prepared by digestion, in nitric acid, of certain concentrates from the uranium ore. The uranyl nitrate solution obtained after removal of impurities is boiled down to a molten uranyl nitrate hexahydrate. The molten salt is denitrated by calcination at about 250–300°C to produce the orange oxide.

By contacting the orange oxide with hydrogen at about 600°C the brown oxide (UO_2) is formed. The latter is converted to green salt by reaction with anhydrous hydrogen fluoride in a furnace.

The green salt is reduced to massive uranium metal in a thermite type of reaction; either calcium or magnesium may be employed as the reducing agent:

$$UF_4 + 2Ca \rightarrow U + 2CaF_2 + 137 \text{ kcal} \qquad (IX.2-1)$$

$$UF_4 + 2Mg \rightarrow U + 2MgF_2 + 84 \text{ kcal} \qquad (IX.2-2)$$

Although calcium has been widely employed as the reductant (and is still used in European countries), a purer uranium metal can be obtained, as is done in the United States, with the use of magnesium. Commercial-grade magnesium generally has fewer undesirable contaminants than commercially obtainable calcium. In addition, calcium is much more expensive and a greater mass is required.

Neither reaction (IX.2-1) nor (IX.2-2) occurs at room temperature. Heat must be applied in order to initiate the reaction. The calcium reduction has the advantage that the heat of reaction is sufficient to melt the uranium and calcium fluoride products, even in the open. The use of magnesium requires a closed vessel, since the temperatures attained during reaction are above the boiling point of magnesium, which would be lost if no closure were employed. Because of the lower heat of reaction with magnesium, extra heat energy must generally be

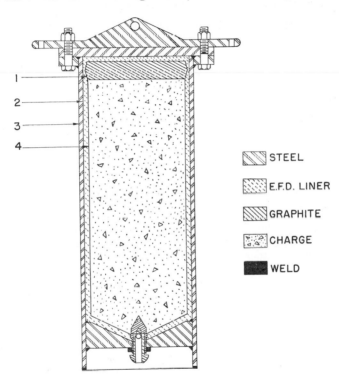

▨ STEEL

▧ E.F.D. LINER

▨ GRAPHITE

▨ CHARGE

■ WELD

(1) GRAPHITE CAKE. (2) REFRACTORY LINER. (3) BOMB WALL.
(4) CHARGE OF UF₄ AND Mg.

Fig. IX.2-1. *Bomb ready for a uranium reduction.*

employed, before or during the reaction, to attain the necessary temperature for fusion. One effective way has been to ignite small amounts of potassium chlorate (KClO₃) mixed with the finely ground green salt and granular magnesium. Simple preheating of the green salt–magnesium mixture to about 550–700°C is probably simpler and less expensive.

The boiling point of magnesium is well below the temperatures attained in the reduction process. This makes it essential, in order to retain the reductant, that the process be carried out in a closed vessel. Steel bombs are generally employed. In order to prevent interaction between the charge and the bomb, a finely ground refractory material, such as calcium or magnesium oxide, is used as a bomb liner. A thick graphite disc is generally employed to protect the bomb closure from the action of the charge (see Fig. IX.2-1).

The dense liquid uranium collects in a pool at the bottom of the bomb, the lighter molten magnesium fluoride slag at the top. After cooling, the contents are removed. The metal is easily separated from slag and liner material. Ingots of uranium are then formed by vacuum casting of the "biscuits" of uranium obtained in the reduction process. This further helps in the purification of the uranium by removal of slag particles and hydrogen.

IX.3. THE METALLURGY OF URANIUM

Pure uranium is a dense, hard, gray-white metal with a distinct luster when freshly prepared. It is a relatively weak metal when hot, but when worked cold its strength may approach that of steel. Some of its physical properties are listed in Table IX.3-1.

TABLE IX.3-1

SOME PHYSICAL PROPERTIES OF URANIUM

Density	19.05 gm/cm^3
Melting Point	1132°C
Boiling Point	3818°C (est.)
Transformation Temperatures	
$\alpha \rightarrow \beta$	668°C
$\beta \rightarrow \gamma$	774°C

Uranium is quite reactive chemically. It tarnishes readily in air, forming a loosely adherent oxide film. This requires that the treatment of small or thin pieces of uranium at high temperatures be undertaken either in a vacuum or in an inert atmosphere. Because of the rapid reaction with oxygen, which produces heat, finely divided uranium is pyrophoric.

Uranium exhibits a high degree of anisotropy in many of its properties. This is a result of the fact that many properties of uranium, such as its strength and thermal expansion, are a function of crystal orientation. This is further complicated in that uranium exists in three different crystalline forms: alpha (orthorhombic structure), beta (tetragonal), and gamma (body-centered cubic). Models are shown in Fig. IX.3-1. This fact has a significant influence on the treatment and behavior of fuel elements at elevated temperatures. The alpha phase is stable below 668°C and the gamma phase from 774°C to the melting point; the beta phase is stable between 668° and 774°C.

The low degree of symmetry of the orthorhombic structure of uranium, unique among metals, leads to a considerable anisotropy in the alpha phase. This has, for example, important consequences with regard to its thermal expansion. In

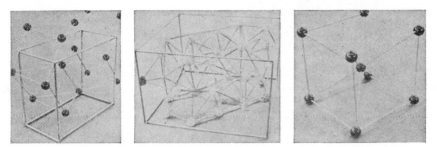

FIG. IX.3-1. *Models of the crystal structures of the uranium allotropes: alpha, left; beta, center; and gamma, right.* [*Reprinted from J. P. Howe, Paper No.* 825, Proc. Intl. Conf. Atomic Energy, *United Nations, N. Y.* (1950), *Vol.* 9, *p.* 191.]

two of the directions, the crystal increases in dimensions with rise in temperature, whereas in the third there is a decrease. Upon heating and cooling in the range from room temperature to a temperature below 660°C, polycrystalline alpha uranium undergoes considerable distortion if the crystals are not randomly

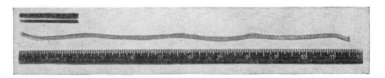

FIG. IX.3-2. *Comparison of a test piece before and after* 3000 *cycles between* 50 *and* 600 *C.*

oriented, because the individual grains prefer to expand more in certain directions than in others and yet are restrained by neighboring crystals from contracting to their original positions. In cast metal, which has randomly oriented crystals if quickly cooled, the changes manifest themselves in the form of surface roughening, although the overall dimensions may be nearly constant. In wrought metal, such as rolled rod or wire, many of the crystals tend to be similarly oriented by the working, and in this case heating and cooling produces substantial elongation (see Fig. IX.3-2). This anisotropy effect of alpha uranium gives rise to many problems of stability in reactors.

Uranium can be fabricated by conventional means, including casting, rolling, extrusion, forging, swaging, drawing, and machining. The mechanical properties are quite dependent on the method of fabrication. Hot-rolling of the alpha phase is a useful method for forming the metal. Each of the above treatments may lead

Uranium, As Cast

Uranium, Cold Worked by Swaging

**Uranium, Cold Worked and Heated
in Lead at 475°C for 10 Minutes**

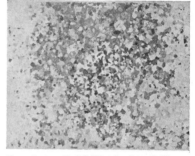

Uranium, Cold Worked and Heated
in Lead at 525°C for 10 Minutes

Uranium, Cold Worked and Heated
in Salt at 725°C for 10 Minutes

Uranium, Cold Worked and Heated
in Salt at 825°C for 10 Minutes

FIG. IX.3-3. *Photomicrographs showing the internal structure of uranium
specimens treated in various manners.*

to a different grain structure of the uranium. Some illustrations of this are shown
for the alpha phase in Fig. IX.3-3. Thus techniques of fabrication and subsequent heat treatments are important factors in determining the extent of

distortion that may occur in a given fuel element. If uranium is prepared by a process which results in random orientation of the crystals and a fine grain size, the uranium does not grow on heating and cooling and its surface remains smooth.

If a uranium rod rolled in the alpha phase, so that it would grow considerably upon thermal cycling, is heated above 668°C, so that the beta phase forms, the alpha structure to which it returns on cooling is nearly randomly oriented and the growth on thermal cycling is considerably reduced. This beta treatment removes substantially the preferred grain orientations present in the rolled rods. It is this preferred orientation produced in rolling that is responsible for the unidirectional elongation.

IX.4. RADIATION DAMAGE TO URANIUM

A fuel material is subjected to damage from both fast neutrons and fission fragments. As a result of their kinetic energies, fission fragments may interact with the atoms of the parent fuel The range of the fission fragments is of the

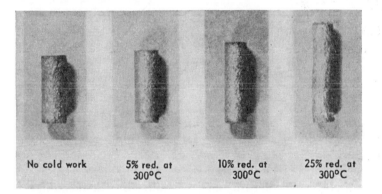

No cold work   5% red. at   10% red. at   25% red. at
                300°C   300°C   300°C

Fig. IX.4-1. *Effect of 0.1 atom per cent burnup on uranium rolled at 600° C and quenched in the beta phase. The samples had been cold worked at 300° C to the reductions indicated.*

order of microns. As the fission fragments move they produce ionization effects.

Vacant lattice sites in a fuel element may be created either by collisions of fission fragments or of energetic neutrons with the atoms in a solid lattice. The energy transferred in these collisions is usually sufficient to permit the recoiling atom to create further vacant lattice sites by subsequent collisions. Thus for each primary collision a cascade of collisions resulting in vacancies is initiated.

The fission product atoms themselves are impurities in the fuel. Since their total atomic volumes are greater than that of the uranium atom, at the very minimum a corresponding increase in the volume of the system may be anticipated.

Most of the damage to uranium appears in the forms of embrittlement, distortion, and growth. One of the most spectacular effects is the radical change in the dimensions of test specimens. Some of the effects may be similar to those

Beta Quenched Uranium Before Irradiation   Beta Quenched Uranium After Irradiation

(100 diameters, polarized light)

Fig. IX.4-2. *Photomicrographs showing the effect of irradiation on the metallographic structure of uranium.*

observed as the result of thermal cycling, and there may also be cracking or swelling. The techniques used for fabrication coupled with subsequent heat treatments have been found to be important factors in determining the resistance of uranium to distortion by irradiation (see Fig. IX.4-1). The metallographic appearance of polycrystalline uranium is also altered by irradiation (for example, see Fig. IX.4-2). In the structure before irradiation the grains are sharply outlined by polarized light; after irradiation the structure appears to be badly distorted as if by cold work.

Other properties of uranium are affected. The density has been found to decrease, as is also true of the thermal and electric conductivities. The tensile properties are affected in such a manner as to destroy for all practical purposes the ductility of the metal. Appreciable hardness changes occur.

It is common metallurgical knowledge that the properties of base metals may be altered and improved by the addition of alloying elements. The severe radiation damage observed in metallic uranium has led to the use, in some cases, of various alloys, such as that of uranium with aluminum. For both metallurgical and nuclear reasons niobium, zirconium, and molybdenum have also been utilized as alloying agents. The crystal structures of many of these alloys are much less susceptible to radiation damage.

In the case of aluminum there is a eutectic transformation occurring at about 13 weight per cent (w/o) uranium (see the phase diagram given in Fig. IX.4-3). In this neighborhood the uranium shows the highest degree of uniform dispersion

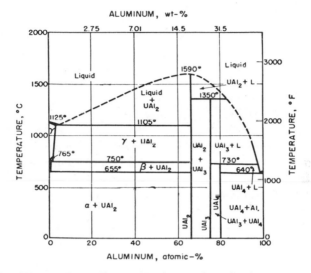

FIG. IX.4-3. *Phase diagram for the uranium-aluminum system.*

in the aluminum. No serious changes occur in the aluminum-uranium alloy even after one atom in a thousand has undergone fission, whereas serious damage is observed in uranium metal after one atom in ten thousand has fissioned. This better behavior of the alloy can be attributed to the dispersion of the uranium in a metal well suited to absorb the damage from the fast neutrons and the process of fission.

Chapter X

PROCESSING OF REACTOR FUELS

X.1. SEPARATIONS CHEMISTRY

One of the practical problems which must be overcome in the field of nuclear energy and its applications is in obtaining suitable procedures of chemistry and chemical engineering for what may be called "separations processes." With our present knowledge, the processing of highly radioactive materials, such as a fuel element removed from a reactor, is costly. Highly specialized facilities and expensive instrumentation are required. Cheap and safe methods must be found for separating a desired product from other substances considered contaminants. In general, such methods as are useful in ordinary processes, like the separation of macro amounts of impurities from macro amounts of product (e.g., the separation of silica from an iron ore), are not suitable in the field of nuclear energy, for requirements of purity are often orders of magnitudes higher than in industrial processes. Whereas a trace amount of contaminant or impurity may be of no concern in ordinary chemical practice, in many cases such extremely small amounts of material may exert enormous influences if used in the construction of a reactor or in determining the cross sections for neutron interactions of a given substance.

For example, consider the fuel which is removed from a reactor. It still contains an appreciable amount of fissionable material. New fissionable species, such as plutonium-239, may also be present. For economic operations of reactors, these must be recovered.

It was seen in § VIII.6 that 1 megawatt-day of operation of a reactor utilizes slightly more than 1 gm of uranium-235. This leads to the formation of roughly 1 gm of fission products. If it is assumed that uranium-238 may be converted to plutonium-239 with 100 per cent efficiency, so that every fission of a uranium-235 nucleus provides one neutron for this transformation, then about 1 gm of plutonium-239 will be present. Since the amount of burnup of the uranium fuel is small before the fuel must be replaced (because of dimensional changes, structural damage, too high an absorption of neutrons by the fission products, etc.), the spent fuel element contains only a relatively small amount of plutonium and fission products dispersed in a comparatively large mass of uranium. After 10,000 megawatt-days per ton of operation of a thermal power reactor there would be about 15 pounds of plutonium and 22 pounds of fission products in a ton of uranium. In this amount of fission products there may be almost two hundred isotopes of more than thirty elements.

All of the familiar types of ordinary chemical processing may have to be used in order to obtain clean and efficient recovery or separation. It is necessary to separate gases from gases, gases from liquids, liquids from liquids, liquids from solids, solids from solids, and solids from gases. When it is appreciated that concentrations of substances under consideration may be as small as 10^{-15} times less than solutions normally regarded as of extreme dilution, some modifications of normal procedures are to be expected.

X.2. PRECIPITATION METHODS

Precipitation methods have long been used by chemists for the separation of elements or for the removal of impurities from a desired product. The concentrations of plutonium and the fission products present in solutions derived from spent fuel elements from production reactors (fuel burnups of 600 megawatt-days per ton) are so small as compared with uranium, however, that direct precipitation as usually employed in analytical procedures is not practicable. Frequently the concentration is so low that the addition of a precipitating agent does not cause the solubility product of a compound of the trace element to be exceeded or, if it does, the precipitate formed is imperceptible. For example, the amounts of several radioactive nuclides undergoing 10,000 disintegrations per minute, an easily measurable rate, are listed as follows.

1590-yr Ra^{226}	2×10^{-11} gm-atom
140-d Po^{212}	5×10^{-15} gm-atom
10.6-hr Pb^{212}	1.5×10^{-17} gm-atom
3.1-min Tl^{208}	7.5×10^{-20} gm-atom (about 45,000 atoms)

It is clear that ordinary procedures involving precipitation and filtration or centrifugation may fail.

The problem may be solved by the use of a *carrier:* a substance (usually not radioactive) added in an appreciable amount to a solution such that a trace element will follow it or be "carried along" with it in a desired chemical procedure. Thus an inactive isotope of the element being separated could be deliberately added as a carrier; the chemical problems then become ordinary macroscopic problems. It is, of course, necessary that the two isotopes be in the same chemical form. If one existed as, say, I^- and the other as IO_3^-, the advantages of the carrying action would be lost (barring the existence of a rapid isotopic exchange reaction).

If necessary or desirable (for example, to prevent a decrease of specific activity), nonisotopic carriers can be used. Thus if lanthanum is added to a solution and its fluoride precipitated, trace amounts of trivalent plutonium that may be present will be carried down with it. Microscopic amounts of radium in solution were traditionally brought down with barium by precipitation of barium sulfate.

The simplest explanation of the phenomenon of carrying is that the trace element becomes incorporated into the crystal lattice of a carrier precipitate in the form of a solid solution. This will occur, in general, when the precipitated salts of the trace element and the carrier are isomorphous (that is, they occur in the same crystalline form) and the ions of the two elements are not greatly different in size. Ions of the trace element replace ions of the carrier element at their normal sites in the crystal lattice. For example, CuS can usually be counted on to carry traces of ions such as bismuth, lead, or mercuric ions, which also form acid-insoluble sulfides. In such cases the carried element is distributed throughout the precipitate crystals, as may be shown by a radioautographic technique. This true coprecipitation of the isomorphous replacement type is not greatly affected by conditions during precipitation. The ratio of the fraction of tracer to the fraction of carrier removed from solution is relatively constant over a wide range of concentrations.

Many precipitates, especially when freshly formed, possess large surface areas. Appreciable amounts of trace elements may then be effectively carried by adsorption. Such a precipitate is called a scavenger. Gelatinous ferric hydroxide or aluminum hydroxide have been widely employed for such purposes. In such circumstances there is no obvious relation between the carrier precipitate and the material carried. Thus barium and zirconium will be carried by precipitating lanthanum fluoride from an acid solution. As an approximate rule, highly charged positive ions are more readily adsorbed than those of a lower charge.

Carrying by adsorption is greatly dependent on the conditions existing at the time of formation of the precipitate. The order of addition of reagents, the presence of inert substances, the various concentrations, the rate of mixing, the temperature, and so forth will affect the quantity of the trace element adsorbed by the carrier. Many of these factors determine the nature and magnitude of the surface area of the precipitate and thus the fraction of tracer adsorbed.

Many precipitation methods for the separation of plutonium and fission products from the uranium of a spent reactor fuel have been worked out. Most of them depend on the fact that the simple hexavalent salts of uranium and plutonium are usually soluble in water, whereas many of their tetravalent compounds are insoluble. Thus plutonium can be separated from uranium by carrier precipitation as a tetravalent salt if the uranium is kept in the hexavalent state. As has been indicated, lanthanum is a good carrier for plutonium.

Some of the fission products will be carried down with the plutonium. A separation can be effected by dissolving the precipitate, oxidizing the plutonium to the hexavalent state, and reprecipitating the carrier, which will bring along the fission product impurities.

X.3. ION EXCHANGE

Certain solids, called *ion exchangers*, although themselves insoluble in water, are able to exchange either positive or negative ions with ions of the same charge present in an aqueous solution. Such materials in most general use are based on synthetic resins, consisting of insoluble organic polymers of high molecular weight, called ion exchange resins.

In general an ion exchange resin consists of a loosely cross-linked, polymerized organic structure to which are attached a number of active (or functional) groups. In cation exchange resins the functional group is acidic in character, such as the carboxylic groups ($-COOH$), phenolic ($-OH$), or sulfonic acid ($-SO_3H$) groups, capable of splitting off a hydrogen ion. In anion exchange resins the active group, such as the amino ($-NX_2$), imino ($-NX$), or quarternary ammonium ($-NX_3^+$) groups, is basic; here X symbolizes a hydrogen or organic radical. In Dowex-50 or Amberlite IR-120, which have been widely used, the functional group is the strongly acidic sulfonic acid group.

The exceedingly useful technique of separation by ion exchange is particularly applicable to dilute solutions of chemically similar substances (such as the rare earth or the transuranic elements) that are difficult to separate by other methods. It can be used for such purposes as (a) removal of substances from a solution, (b) altering the concentrations of substances in solution, (c) replacement of one ion in solution by another, and (d) separation of ions from one another. The process is generally carried out with a fixed resin bed through which the solution percolates. The interchange occurs between the ions in solution and the mobile ions of the same sign from the ion exchange resin.

For example, a cationic resin, which may be symbolized H-R, can be used to exchange with positive ions in an equilibrium reaction:

$$n \text{ H-R (resin)} + M^{n+} \text{ (solution)} \rightleftarrows M\text{-}R_n \text{ (resin)} + n H^+ \text{ (solution).} \quad \text{(X.3-1)}$$

Similarly, for an anionic resin, say R-Cl,

$$n \text{ R-Cl (resin)} + A^{n-} \text{ (solution)} \rightleftarrows R_n\text{-}A \text{ (resin)} + n \text{ Cl}^- \text{ (solution).} \quad \text{(X.3-2)}$$

Since the resins have a limited capacity for sorbing ions they are not too suitable for the removal of ions present at high concentrations. The ability of a resin to retain different ions under given conditions is determined by two factors: the charge on the ion, on one hand, and the size of the hydrated ion in solution, on the other. The greater the charge, either positive or negative as the appropriate case may be, carried by the ion and the smaller the radius of the ion *in the hydrated form* the more strongly will the ion be retained by a given resin. (If ionic equilibria exist in solution these rules may be modified to some extent.)

In practice a solution containing the ions to be separated is allowed to percolate down a column containing the finely divided resin. In the first stage of the process the solution ions replace the mobile ions of the same sign on the resin and become adsorbed, usually in a thin band near the top of the column.

The elution stage represents the actual separation step. A suitable eluting solution (or eluent or elutrient) is allowed to percolate slowly through the ion exchange column containing the sorbed ions. The adsorbed ions are continually removed and redeposited as the eluent flows down the column. The rates with which different ionic species move down the column are different because the stabilities of the resin compounds are different. Even though this difference in sorption on the resin may not be very great, the repeated sorption and desorption amplifies the small difference into an efficient separation. (For example, a partial separation of the lithium isotopes has been effected by ion exchange methods.)

If the eluent has been properly chosen there is a degree of selectivity in these processes of sorption and desorption, so that the liquid emerging from the bottom of the column (the eluate) will contain first one and then another of the ions in a relatively pure form. If the ion concentrations in the eluate are determined as a function of time, the results will be somewhat as shown in Fig. X.3-1. It is seen that the ions A are eluted first. In this manner the various ions can be collected separately in successive fractions of the effluent.

The retention of a particular ionic species for a given resin may be expressed by the distribution coefficient, K_d, which is the ratio of the concentration of the ion in the resin to that in the solution at equilibrium:

$$K_d = \frac{\text{concentration of ion in resin}}{\text{concentration of ion in solution}}. \qquad \text{(X.3-3)}$$

The separation factor α for two given ionic species A and B is defined as the ratio of the distribution coefficients for the particular resin:

$$\alpha = \frac{K_d(B)}{K_d(A)} \qquad \text{(X.3-4)}$$

$$= \frac{\text{conc. of B in resin}}{\text{conc. of A in resin}} \times \frac{\text{conc. of A in soln.}}{\text{conc. of B in soln.}}$$

If α is large, the species B will tend to remain in the resin, so that ions of species A will be the first to leave the column in the elution stage.

If α is of the order of unity, the separation technique will not be efficient. The value of α may be altered, for example, by employing an elution solution containing anions which form complexes with A and B of differing stabilities. Thus if the complex formed with A is stronger than that formed with B, the ratio of free ions of B to free ions of A in the solution becomes large; this raises the value of α and a good separation may be obtained.

In Fig. X.3-1 it is seen that there is an intermediate region in which the eluate contains both ions A and B. The extent of this region of overlap is the smaller the greater the value of the separation factor α and the longer the length of the column in which the fractionation occurs.

A slow flow rate, a high ratio of resin to ion, and a fine size of the resin particles favor close approach to equilibrium. All of these increase the time required to effect the separation. In practice a compromise is generally made between the conditions for obtaining a large value of the separation factor (and thus a good yield) and speed.

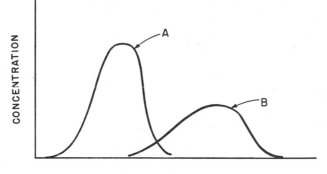

FIG. X.3-1. *Elution curve for two ions, A and B.*

Solutions of spent fuel elements contain high concentrations of uranium and very small concentrations of plutonium and fission products. A possible method of separation would be to pass such a solution through a resin which absorbed the plutonium and the fission products but not the uranium. The plutonium could then be eluted in a suitable manner. Another possibility would be to find such conditions that only the plutonium was sorbed, the uranium and the fission products passing out with the effluent. The fission products themselves have been separated by ion exchange procedures without resort to carriers.

One of the most striking applications of ion exchange procedures has been the separation of rare earths from each other, both on a tracer scale and in macro amounts. By this means the 3000 to 4000 laborious fractional crystallization steps formerly employed, with much loss of product, have been avoided.

The choice of an ion exchange resin for a given process with radioactive materials is often made in terms of the effects of radiation damage. This is generally exhibited by a loss in capacity. However, other effects include changes in the physical and chemical characters.

X.4. SOLVENT EXTRACTION

The fact that a solute will distribute itself between two immiscible solvents has been used to great effect. The extraction of iodine from its aqueous solutions by the use of carbon tetrachloride is a familiar experiment. The extraction of uranyl nitrate from aqueous solutions into ether or some other suitable solvent has been used as a convenient method for the separation of fission products from the bulk of uranium in solutions of spent reactor fuel elements. As compared with ion exchange, solvent extraction has the disadvantage of smaller mass-transfer efficiency. On the other hand, separation factors are frequently larger. A more practical advantage of solvent-extraction procedures is that they are not limited to dilute solutions.

As in the case of ion exchange, the distribution coefficient K_d is defined as the equilibrium ratio of the concentrations in the two immiscible phases:

$$K_d = \frac{\text{concentration of component in organic phase}}{\text{concentration of component in aqueous phase}}. \qquad \text{(X.4-1)}$$

Similarly, the separation factor between two components, A and B, is given by the ratio of the two distribution coefficients:

$$\alpha = \frac{K_d(\text{component B})}{K_d(\text{component A})} \qquad \text{(X.4-2)}$$

$$= \frac{\text{conc. of B in organic soln.}}{\text{conc. of A in organic soln.}} \times \frac{\text{conc. of A in aq. soln.}}{\text{conc. of B in aq. soln.}}$$

A good solvent for extraction is thus one for which the separation factor is large. It is also desirable that the organic liquid should be almost completely immiscible with the aqueous solution. This is generally impossible in practice, since all liquids exhibit some mutual solubility. Of course, the organic liquid should be chemically stable with respect to possible reagents, such as oxidizing or reducing agents employed in the process. In dealing with radioactive solvents, the organic solvent must be stable with respect to nuclear radiations, which may often be intense.

In order that the two liquid phases may separate readily after contact, the organic solvent should have a density which differs appreciably from that of the aqueous solution. The greater the difference the more rapidly will the phases tend to separate.

The surface tension between the two liquids should be sufficiently high to prevent the formation of a stable emulsion. If it is too high, however, it will be difficult to attain a good dispersion of one liquid phase into the other.

X.5. NONAQUEOUS METHODS

Although aqueous methods of processing are highly effective in giving high purity, they are also expensive and require large volumes of intensely radioactive solutions to be handled. Accordingly new approaches are being investigated. Although these have not yet been adopted for actual plants, they do give promise of proving to be more economical and advantageous.

The separation of elements or of their compounds by making use of differences in vapor pressure has been widely employed for years, such as in distillation procedures, and may be applied to the separation of radioactive materials.

Uranium hexafluoride (UF_6) is a readily volatile solid (subliming at 56.5°C), whereas the trifluoride (UF_3) and the tetrafluoride (UF_4) are nonvolatile. Many of the fluorides of the fission products are essentially nonvolatile. This offers the possibility of devising a method for their separaiton. Several approaches being tried use various fluorinating agents such as fluorine, bromine trifluoride (BrF_3), or chlorine trifluoride (ClF_3) to produce the volatile fluorides. Advantage is then taken of the differences in volatilities to effect separations.

Plutonium itself can be concentrated by vacuum distillation from molten uranium at 1500° to 1800°C.

Metallurgical procedures are being investigated for the treatment of spent reactor fuels. Techniques for removing the fission products and recovering the plutonium directly from the metal include volatilization, metal-metal extraction, precipitation, solid slagging, fused salt scrubbing, and electrorefining. Among the advantages of such pyrometallurgical methods are the relative stability to radiation, the comparatively short time needed for processing, and the small volume of fission product wastes. In addition, since such schemes avoid bulk chemical conversion during purification, the usual need for converting uranium or plutonium salts back to the metal are avoided. All of these can be used to obtain lower costs for processing than are now available by aqueous techniques.

In melt-refining processes the fuel material is placed in a suitable container (generally a crucible of some refractory oxide or of graphite), heated, and held in the molten state for a comparatively long period of time before being cast into ingots for refabrication into fuel elements. Some of the fission products (such as cesium and xenon) escape from the liquid metal because of their volatility. Others, such as strontium, may be preferentially oxidized by reaction with the crucible material, and removed as a slag. Still others, such as molybdenum and ruthenium, are not removed, but a certain amount may be tolerated or may even be beneficial in the new fuel element. If their concentrations build up, they may be removed or reduced in amounts by various special means.

Solvent extraction processes employing liquid magnesium in contact with liquid uranium have been devised. The plutonium, for example, will redistribute itself preferentially in the liquid magnesium, from which it can be separated in a subsequent distillation process. Extraction of plutonium from liquid uranium by fused salts has also been successfully accomplished.

Coprecipitation of trace elements with carrier elements from molten metallic solutions has also been employed as a separations procedure.

Chapter XI

THE EFFECTS OF RADIATIONS UPON MATERIALS

XI.1. RADIATION CHEMISTRY

Ionizing radiations of different energies and masses cause a variety of physical, chemical, and biological effects. A knowledge of such changes is of great practical importance in the applications of nuclear energy. *Radiation chemistry* is the study of the chemical effects of nuclear particles and radiations on matter. (This subject should be distinguished from radiochemistry, which is the study of chemical reactions in which radioactive atoms are taking part.)

For the most part, chemical reactions may be essentially unaffected by moderate intensities of radiation. However, it has long been known that some chemical reactions cannot even occur under ordinary conditions; they require light to fall upon the reactants before the process will take place. Such reactions are called photochemical, since the energy of the light is required to bring about the reaction. In many cases the light does not act as a mere stimulus or catalyst, but is an integral part of the reaction.

If a photochemical reaction proceeds when light of a definite frequency falls on the substances, it is usually found that the yield of the reaction changes or may drop to zero with a relatively small change in the frequency. The frequency of the radiation is thus characteristic of the reaction. Thus, light ranging from the green to the ultraviolet and beyond can affect a photographic plate, but red light produces little effect. Again, photosynthesis in plants requires both red and blue light.

In photography (Scheele observed the darkening of AgCl by light in 1777), light or any ionizing radiation or particle will, on absorption in the emulsion of a photographic plate or film, produce activation of the silver halide grains, that is, make them developable. It may be recalled that the photographic procedure was the basis of the historical method whereby radioactivity was discovered and detected, when Becquerel found that uranium could cause fogging of photographic plates.

Radiation chemistry is closely related to photochemistry; in a broad sense there is no distinction between the two. One important difference is the great complexity of radiation chemistry. This is due not so much to the fundamental difference in the nature of the excited molecules that are formed or the types of primary and secondary reactions that occur, but to the greater number of different types of molecules that may be excited by very energetic radiation. In a photochemical study, light of the proper wavelength is selected to excite only one type of molecule in the system; energetic radiations, on the other hand, are not absorbed as one unit, in general, as is a light photon, but expend their energies along their paths nonselectively by ionizing and exciting molecules of all types. These excited molecules and ions may participate in radiation-induced reactions that are not possible for unexcited molecules. In photochemistry, the concern is with radiations of comparatively small energies.

Photochemistry has helped to clarify the processes of radiation chemistry and reaction kinetics by allowing an intercomparison of the behavior of aqueous systems irradiated by light and by ionizing radiations. Two points of difference are: (1) light should give pairs of radicals randomly distributed throughout the solution, whereas ionizing radiations should yield clusters of radicals; and (2) ionizing radiations give both ions and excited molecules with varying energies, while monochromatic light yields species of some definite energy in the primary act.

XI.2. YIELDS OF RADIATION CHEMICAL PROCESSES

The yield of products of a chemical reaction caused by the action of radiation on a chemical system is determined by (1) the elementary processes brought about by the absorbed radiation and the primary chemical products (ions, atoms, radicals, and excited atoms or molecules) formed, and (2) the secondary processes (recombinations, chemical reactions with solvent or solute, chain reactions, etc.). In photochemistry yields are usually expressed in terms of a quantum yield, or quantum efficiency, sometimes symbolized by Φ, and defined as the ratio of the number of molecules of a substance decomposed to the number of photons absorbed by the system.

It has been emphasized (see § II.1) that the principal process in the interaction between radiation and matter is one of ionization. It was formerly believed that the energy liberated on the neutralization or recombination of the ions was responsible for the reactions attributed to radiations. Accordingly the yields of such reactions were generally reported in terms of a ratio M/N, where M symbolized the number of reacting molecules and N the number of ion pairs formed by the radiation. It is now generally accepted, however, that the excitation of electrons in molecules by the radiation may be of much more importance than any excitation of the molecule which might result from the neutralization of ions. At the present time yields are usually given in terms of a quantity symbolized by G and defined as the number of molecules produced or converted per 100 ev of energy expended by the radiation. Yields are usually of the order of 1 molecule per 10 to 20 ev, thus representing a rather inefficient utilization of the energy. Some examples are given in Table XI.2-1. In the table, the yields of H and OH are being ignored for the case of water.

TABLE XI.2-1

YIELDS OF SOME RADIATION-INDUCED DECOMPOSITIONS

Molecule Decomposed	Products	Radiation	G
$H_2O(liq)$	H_2, O_2, H_2O_2	1-Mev β	0.4
		5-Mev α	2.0
		fast neutrons	
		and gammas	
		from reactor	1.0
$Fe^{+++}(aq)$	Fe^{++}	β,γ	0.6
$AgI(aq)$	$Ag(s)$	β,γ	0.3
$CCl_4(1)$	Cl_2	β,γ	0.6

XI.3. RADIATION DECOMPOSITION OF WATER

Because water is so widely used in reactors, the actions of nuclear radiations upon this material are of particular interest. Water absorbs energy from the radiations to form atoms, radicals, and ions, an undesirable process from the viewpoint of reactor operations. The net effect is that gaseous H_2 and O_2 are liberated, and H_2O_2 can be detected in the aqueous phase.

The primary reactive species are believed to be H and OH, as manifested by their reactions with solutes, although HO_2 and H_2O_2 are formed later. It seems that within a time interval of about 10^{-12} second after the passage of an ionizing particle through water, an equal number of H and OH radicals are formed; these may be generated from the ions H_2O^+ and H_2O^- produced by the radiation or generated directly by the dissociation of an excited water molecule, H_2O^*:

$$H_2O^+ + H_2O \rightarrow H_3O^+ + OH \tag{XI.3-1}$$

$$H_2O^- \rightarrow H + OH^- \tag{XI.3-2}$$

$$H_2O^* \rightarrow H + OH. \tag{XI.3-3}$$

If the specific ionization of the radiation is small, as it is with gamma rays, the H and OH radicals are formed in separate clusters, having, perhaps, three pairs of these radicals, on the average, per cluster. The H and OH have a better chance to escape and react with H_2, H_2O_2, or H_2O, than to recombine to form H_2, H_2O_2, or H_2O by the reactions

$$H + H \rightarrow H_2, \tag{XI.3-5}$$

and

$$OH + OH \rightarrow H_2O_2. \tag{XI.3-6}$$

If the radiation has a high specific ionization, there is a greater extent of such recombination to form H_2, H_2O_2, and H_2O. (However, it has been observed that as the energy of the alpha particle increases, so does the yield of radicals; this is associated with a decrease of the specific ionization of the more energetic alpha particles.) With radiations of intermediate specific ionization, the yields of radicals and molecules may vary smoothly from one extreme to the other.

The free atom H is a powerful reducing agent, and the free radical OH is a powerful oxidizing agent. These lead to various oxidation and reduction reactions with the substances present:

$$H + OH \rightarrow H_2O \qquad\qquad (XI.3-4)$$

$$H + H \rightarrow H_2 \qquad\qquad (XI.3-5)$$

$$OH + OH \rightarrow H_2O_2 \qquad\qquad (XI.3-6)$$

$$H_2O_2 + H \rightarrow H_2O + OH \qquad\qquad (XI.3-7)$$

$$H_2O_2 + OH \rightarrow HO_2 + H_2O \qquad\qquad (XI.3-8)$$

$$H_2 + OH \rightarrow H_2O + H. \qquad\qquad (XI.3-9)$$

This complex set of reactions leads to the formation and destruction of H_2 and H_2O_2 as the decomposition products of water. For low specific ionizations, the destruction limits the H_2 and H_2O_2 to low steady-state values. Apparently the O_2 which is frequently observed is formed rather slowly from H_2O_2:

$$H_2O_2 \rightarrow H_2O + \tfrac{1}{2}O_2 \qquad\qquad (XI.3-10)$$

or from reactions such as

$$HO_2 + HO_2 \rightarrow H_2O_2 + O_2 \qquad\qquad (XI.3-11)$$

and

$$H_2O_2 + HO_2 \rightarrow H_2O + OH + O_2. \qquad\qquad (XI.3-12)$$

XI.4. RADIATION DECOMPOSITION OF AQUEOUS SOLUTIONS AND PURE ORGANIC COMPOUNDS

The discussion in the preceding section with regard to water illustrates the complexity of the chemistry that may be induced by nuclear radiations, even for simple substances. If impurities are present in the water or if we are dealing with an aqueous solution, then still many more reactions are possible. If, for example, ferrous ions are present, some possible reactions are

$$Fe^{++} + OH \rightarrow Fe^{+++} + OH^- \qquad\qquad (XI.4-1)$$

$$Fe^{++} + H_2O_2 \rightarrow Fe^{+++} + OH^- + OH \qquad\qquad (XI.4-2)$$

$$Fe^{++} + H^+ + HO_2 \rightarrow Fe^{+++} + H_2O_2 \qquad\qquad (XI.4-3)$$

$$Fe^{+++} + HO_2 \rightarrow Fe^{++} + O_2 + H^+ \qquad\qquad (XI.4-4)$$

$$Fe^{++} + H + H^+ \rightarrow H_2 + Fe^{+++} \qquad\qquad (XI.4-5)$$

$$Fe^{+++} + H \rightarrow Fe^{++} + H^+. \qquad\qquad (XI.4-6)$$

If reducing agents are present, these react readily with OH radicals, as exemplified by Equation XI.4-1, thereby lowering the molecular yield of H_2O_2. The presence of oxidizing agents lowers the molecular yield of H_2 through removal of H atoms, as in Equation XI.4-6. Some scavengers protect H_2 and H_2O_2 by scavenging H and OH. At large concentrations such actions may interfere with reactions of Equations XI.3-5 and XI.3-6.

A solution of $FeSO_4$ in 0.8 N H_2SO_4 has been widely used for measuring the intensity of radiations, especially of gamma rays. It is based on the radiation-induced oxidation of Fe^{++} to Fe^{+++} and the important observation that the yield is unchanged over a wide range of concentrations of $FeSO_4$ and the wavelength of the incident radiation, as well as of a wide range of temperature.

Organic compounds in aqueous solution are oxidized by irradiation as a result of the actions of OH radicals. This oxidation is often markedly increased by the presence of dissolved molecular oxygen, presumably due to the oxidizing ability of HO_2 radicals, formed by the reaction:

$$H + O_2 \rightarrow HO_2. \tag{XI.4-7}$$

Formic acid (HCOOH) is oxidized to H_2 and CO_2. In aqueous solution of methanol (CH_3OH), formaldehyde and ethylene glycol may be formed. Small amounts of dissolved benzene give phenol as a product. When most organic materials are subjected to high-energy ionizing sources the result is a breakdown in the molecule and a production of free radicals. This breakdown frequently takes place through the liberation of one or more hydrogen atoms from the molecule. The free radicals formed are, for the most part, extremely reactive. Their stability seems to be dependent upon their mobility, being more stable if produced in the solid state rather than in the liquid state. Generally a complex mixture of products is obtained. Thus, irradiation of benzene will give hydrogen, acetylene, polymeric forms such as diphenyl and terphenyl, and hydrogenated forms of benzene. In general aromatic compounds are more resistant to radiation damage than are aliphatic compounds. Such differences are due to differences in bond strengths and to the nature of the excited states.

XI.5. RADIATION DAMAGE TO SOLIDS

Nuclear radiations may alter drastically the properties of solid materials. The effects of such radiations, generally known as radiation damage, may be conveniently grouped into two categories: the effects produced by ionization or excitation of electrons, and effects produced by displacements of atoms or ions. The four basic types of solids — molecular, ionic, metallic, and valence crystals — behave in rather different ways under bombardment by radiations.

In molecular crystals, for which organic compounds may serve as a good example, the individual molecules are relatively isolated from one another. As a result of changes in the states of the electrons, in general, free radicals and ions are introduced and bonds are rearranged. Plastics are essentially pure organic compounds; it is to be expected that they will be badly affected by radiations because of the breaking down of the covalent bonds. The broken bonds do not generally reform. This has been found to be true in many cases. The use of organic reagents in fuel processing is often limited by the destructive effects of radiation.

In ionic compounds, the energy of excitation of electrons may be converted into displacement of atoms. If the alkali halides are subjected to bombardment by cathode rays or X rays, they are found to darken, each compound acquiring a characteristic color; for example, $NaCl$ becomes yellow and KCl magenta. The reason for this is that some of the electrons that are normally bound to the halogen or alkali metal ions become loosened, wander through the lattice, and eventually become trapped at positions which they would normally not occupy. The color developed is associated either with these displaced electrons or with the unfilled electron shells they leave behind when they are displaced. When crystals which have been discolored by irradiation are heated to a sufficiently high temperature, they bleach to the original colorless state. This process presumably is the result of the recombination of the trapped electrons and positive charges, which is stimulated by the heating process.

In good conductors, such as metals, where electrons possess great freedom of movement, the ionization effects of nuclear radiations disappear very quickly, having no permanent effect, and only contribute to the heating of the material by transfer of energy to the various vibrations occurring in the lattice. Thus beta particles and gamma-ray photons produce little if any radiation damage in electronic conductors.

Bombardment with fast, massive particles (alpha particles, protons, neutrons, fission fragments, etc.), however, produces displacements of atoms from their normal, equilibrium positions in the lattice. Important changes in physical properties arise from the resultant atomic disorder, that is, from the imperfections in the crystal structure, producing strains in the lattice. (The formation of impurity atoms by nuclear transformations may be important.) Among the changes which are produced generally in metals are increases in electrical resistance, in thermal resistance, in hardness, and in tensile strength, accompanied by a decrease in ductility. The effects seem to be less marked on hardened (cold-worked) metals than on those in the annealed condition. Saturation effects also appear. The effects of the radiations are generally smaller at elevated temperatures; further, the effects can generally be removed by raising the temperature (annealing).

Neutrons produced by fission are born with average energies of about 2 Mev. Upon entering a solid a fast neutron produces fast recoil atoms (usually expending a minimum of about 25 ev to displace an atom from its equilibrium position in the crystal lattice of a metal) along its path. This is known as the *Wigner effect*. The recoil atoms in turn produce secondary recoils, etc. The fraction of energy dissipated in ionization decreases rapidly as the recoil atom slows down, and a large portion of the displacement damage is done at the end of the range. (The picture is essentially the same for fission fragments and for accelerated charged particles.)

The displaced atoms leave behind vacant sites in the lattice structure and, if they do not find a vacant site somewhere else in the crystal, finally come to rest in interstitial positions. The net result is a more or less permanent defect in the solid which, if occurring to a sufficient extent, may be accompanied by a change in the physical properties.

A massive particle generally loses a large proportion of its energy within a very small volume. This energy, whether it is removed as an atomic displacement, a lattice vibration, or an electronic excitation, is rapidly converted into heat. The result is the formation of a small region of high temperature, popularly called a *thermal spike*. It has been estimated that the spike will include some 5,000 to 10,000 atoms and that it attains a temperature of 700° to 1200°C for a period of about 10^{-10} second. At such high temperatures, distortion of the lattice, equivalent to local fusion or even vaporization, is to be expected. In the very rapid cooling resulting from the conduction of heat to the surrounding volume, a certain amount of lattice distortion will be frozen into the crystal, since there will not be sufficient time for all the atoms to be relocated in equilibrium positions.

The radiation effects can be removed (annealed) by appropriate heat treatment. An increase of heat means an increase in the thermal vibrations of the lattice atoms and thereby a greater tendency to diffuse. The ease with which such a migration will occur presumably is greatest when the atom is occupying an interstitial site and moves into a vacant equilibrium site. Since a metal which has been exposed to radiation contains both interstitial atoms and vacant sites, there should be a tendency, on raising the temperature, for the former to move into the latter, a sort of recombination process.

As a specific example of a valence crystal with its covalent bonds, consider graphite, which has been used widely as a moderator and as a structural component in nuclear reactors. However, irradiation of graphite in a reactor produces significant changes in its crystalline structure which result in large changes in its physical properties.

The mechanical properties of the graphite seem to be improved; thus, its hardness and strength are increased, although the material becomes more brittle and is more difficult to machine. Other physical properties are detrimentally affected: thermal and electrical conductivities decrease; changes in the gross dimensions occur; several other effects, such as a storing of potential energy, occur. All of these effects are decreased in magnitude, however, when the temperature of the graphite during irradiation is increased.

The major effects of irradiation upon the crystallite structure of graphite, as determined by X-ray diffraction studies, are distortion of the crystal lattice and eventual breakup and disorder of the crystal structure, with a trend toward an amorphous form, reducing the anisotropy. This is produced by bombardment with massive particles; ionizing radiations such as beta and gamma rays are nearly ineffective in producing changes in the properties of graphite. The distortion of the hexagonal, planar structure of the lattice (see Fig. XI.5-1) takes

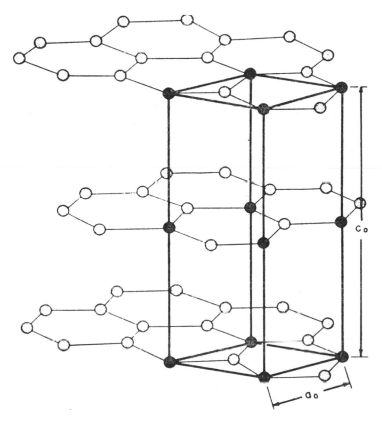

FIG. XI.5-1. *The crystalline structure of graphite. The unit cell has been accented. [Reprinted from W. K. Woods et al., Paper No. 746, Proc. Intl. Conf. Atomic Energy, United Nations, New York, (1956), Vol. 7, p. 460.]*

the form of an expansion in the interplanar (C_0) dimension and a shrinkage or warping of the dimension (a_0) along crystal planes. These distortions are caused primarily by collisions between carbon atoms in the graphite lattice and imping- ing energetic particles, particularly fast neutrons. These collisions result in the displacement of carbon atoms from normal positions within the lattice and the production of lattice vacancies. In addition, the displaced atoms, in losing their kinetic energy, may produce further lattice distortions. Thus, an energetic carbon atom moving through the lattice as a result of a collision with a fast neutron at first loses energy practically solely by electronic excitation and ionization. Below some energy limit, the energy is lost mainly by elastic collisions, in which secondary displaced carbon atoms are produced. The displaced atom finally comes to rest between planes of carbon atoms.

Graphite is a semimetal in which the electric current is carried both by the motions of electrons and "positive holes" (absence of electrons). The resistivity is governed by the concentration of the charge carriers and their mean free paths (average distance between collisions). Both the electrons and the positive holes are scattered by the defects introduced by irradiation, and the mean free paths decrease. The effect is as if the electrons were removed, and thus decreased in concentration, by being trapped in the defects.

The irradiation of the graphite causes an increase in the energy content, called the *stored energy*, of its crystal lattice. It can be observed as an increase in the heat of combustion (as much as several hundred calories per gram) of the material. The stored energy is created because bonds are broken in forming interstitials and vacancies.

Much of the stored energy can be released by annealing at high temperatures. Observation shows that the release of stored energy is associated with a decrease of the expanded interplanar spacing (C_0) toward the normal values for unirradiated graphite. In order to effect complete recovery of either stored energy or lattice distortion in highly irradiated material, it must be haated close to graphitization temperatures.

The recovery process consists of a diffusion of the displaced carbon atoms. These may either move to vacancies or migrate to crystal boundaries.

Many chemical properties of graphite are also affected by irradiation. Thus, the reactions of graphite with gases like oxygen or carbon dioxide are found to be faster after irradiation in a reactor. These effects are probably caused by lattice vacancies (rather than by interstitial atoms), which promote the oxidation of graphite and thereby initiate depressions or pits in the surface.

Chapter XII

BIOLOGY AND RADIATION

XII.1. DOSAGE UNITS

The biological effects of radiation are generally assumed to be almost entirely due to ionization processes causing alterations in various molecules, such as proteins, that play an important part in the functioning of living cells. Actually, the disruption of molecules by recoiling atoms is undoubtedly also a factor, especially in the case of neutron irradiation, but the products and consequences of such processes are not easily isolated for study. Secondary effects exert an influence. Thus the effects of slow neutrons are due almost entirely to their capture by H and N nuclei. The $H(n,\gamma)D$ reaction is accompanied by the emission of 2-Mev photons, some of which may irradiate the surrounding tissue. The $N(n,p)C$ reaction liberates protons.

In determining radiation effects on living organisms, one has to take into consideration not only the total dose of ionization produced in the organism, but also such factors as the specific ionization (see § II.1), the dosage rate, the localization of the ionization, and the rates of administration and elimination of radioactive material.

The units which are used for biological radiation dosage are derived from the roentgen unit, which is named for the discoverer of X rays. One roentgen unit (r) is the quantity of X or gamma radiation such that the associated corpuscular emission per 1.293 mg of air (the mass of 1 cc of dry air under standard conditions of temperature and pressure) produces, in air, ions carrying 1 esu of electricity of either sign (2.08×10^9 ion pairs). This means that 1 roentgen produces 1.61×10^{12} ion pairs per gram of air, which corresponds to the absorption of 83.8 ergs/gm of air. The roentgen is a unit of the total quantity of ionization produced, and dosage rates are expressed in terms of roentgens per unit time. (To get some idea of a roentgen, an X ray of the chest involves about 0.5 r.)

The roentgen is a unit that does not apply to radiations other than X or gamma rays. The roentgen-equivalent-physical (rep) is used to express ionization in tissues caused by other radiations (electrons, protons, alpha particles, neutrons, etc.). One rep is the quantity of ionization produced when 83 ergs are dissipated by the radiation per gram of tissue. Experiments have shown that when 1 roentgen of X or gamma rays is absorbed by the soft tissues of the body, the energy produced is slightly greater than that in air, being actually over 90 ergs/gm; but for practical purposes the absorption of 1 rep of photons is roughly equivalent to 1 roentgen in soft tissue. In bone, which is denser, this would not be true.

The same amount of energy dissipated per gram of tissue may cause different amounts of biological damage, depending upon the different kinds of radiation delivered. For this reason another unit, the roentgen-equivalent-man (rem), is used. One rem corresponds to an energy dissipation which results in dosage biologically equivalent to that produced in man by 1 roentgen of gamma or X rays.

Because of ambiguity as to the amount of energy released in air or water or tissues by the passage of radiation, in 1953 a new unit of absorbed dose, the *rad*, was adopted at the Seventh International Congress of Radiology. A rad was defined as the dosage that will impart 100 ergs to each gram of matter through which the radiation passes. The unit applies to all kinds of radiations.

XII.2. RELATIVE BIOLOGICAL EFFECTIVENESS (RBE)

The ions formed by radiation are not distributed at random but are formed close to the geometrical path of the individual ionizing particle. The spacing of the ions along the track is an important parameter than can influence the biological effectiveness of a given dose. The relative biological efficiencies of different types of radiation may be related empirically through this one parameter.

In general, the greater the specific ionization, the greater the damage from the absorption of a given energy. Physically, the spacing of the ions and excited

TABLE XII.2-1

VALUES OF LD 50/30 DAYS

Organism	Radiation	Dose
Guinea pig	X	175-409 r
Pig	X	275 r
Dog	X	300-430 r
Monkey	X	500 r
Man	X	400-500 r
Rat	X	390-970 r
Rabbit	X	750-825 r
Fowl	X	1000 r
Goldfish	X	670 r
Frog	X	700 r
Tortoise	X	1500 r
Snail	X	8,000-20,000 r
Mouse	X	400-650 r
	Fast neutrons	54 n units*

*An n-unit is a dose of neutrons which produces in a Victoreen ionization chamber the same amount of ionization as 1 roentgen of X rays.

molecules along the track is determined by the magnitude of the charge carried by the ionizing particle (actually proportional to the square of its charge) and by its speed (inverse proportionality). Consequently, protons, deuterons, and electrons (each of the same absolute charge) traveling at equal speeds should produce equal biological effects.

There is a wide range of radiosensitivity among living organisms. In Table XII.2-1, for example, are given values of the LD 50/30 days (that is, the dose of irradiation that kills 50 per cent of the exposed population within 30 days) for various organisms. Further, some tissues of the body are much more sensitive to radiations than others. In general, changes are seen most rapidly among cells that are dividing and reproducing most rapidly. The mechanisms involving cell division and inheritance appear to be among the most sensitive to radiation of any biological system.

Because of the wide range of radiations available and because of the great diversity of biological changes, the concept of *relative biological effectiveness* (RBE) has been introduced. X rays, generated from electrons that have been accelerated to 200 or 250 kv, have been taken as a standard for comparison with other radiation types or qualities. Radiations are compared according to the amount of absorbed energy required to produce a specific biological change. Numerically, RBE is the ratio of the absorbed doses delivered by the standard radiation to the radiation under test:

$$\text{RBE} = \frac{\text{physical dose of 200-kv X rays producing effect}}{\text{physical dose of comparison radiation producing same effect}}.$$

Gamma rays and fission neutrons dissipate their energies through matter in two distinctly different ways. In experiments conducted at Argonne National Laboratory, mice were irradiated for a 90-minute period to fission neutrons and to gamma rays from Co^{60}. Analysis showed that a dose of 210 ± 1 rep of fission neutrons killed one-half of the population. In contrast, a dose of 929 ± 5 rep of gamma rays was necessary to produce the same biological effect. It is thus apparent that the RBE of these two radiations is $929/210 = 4.43$. This means that a dose of fission neutrons is 4.43 times as effective as a physically equivalent dose of Co^{60} gamma rays. By multiplying the neutron dose in rep by the above RBE, dose units are converted to gamma equivalents.

The life span necessarily expresses the combined effects of all the changes caused by irradiation. Mice have been widely used as stand-ins for man in such studies. In general, increasing doses of radiation reduce survival. Alterations in life spans may differ with different radiations and with different genetic backgrounds. Thus, some strains of mice are more resistant to the effects of irradiation than others.

XII.3. RADIATION DAMAGE TO BIOLOGICAL SYSTEMS

The biological effects of exposure to radiation may not appear for weeks or even for years. The nature and the extent of the injuries depend on various circumstances. For example, exposure may be either acute or chronic. *Acute exposure* refers to the receipt of radiation within a short interval of time. *Chronic exposure* is used to describe the frequent (e.g., daily) or continuous exposure. Thus the rate of application of radiation is important in the ultimate biological result.

In general, the shorter the time of application of a given dose of radiation, the more severe the biological effect. Thus, a certain dose of radiation received by an individual in a few seconds may cause harm, whereas the same dose spread over a period of years may produce no noticeable effect. In other words, both the total dose of radiation and the dose rate are important in determining the extent of the biological damage. The smaller the total dose and the dose rate, the less will be the injury. This is part of the reason why radiation may be used in the clinical treatment of certain types of cancers.

In general, chronic exposure to a given total dose has much less serious consequences than acute exposure to the same total dose, because normal tissues, if not seriously damaged, can often repair themselves. Another factor that must also be considered is that total body radiation with a given dose is much more harmful than radiation of a localized part.

It is possible that many of the effects of radiation are of the so-called *threshold type:* the dose received must exceed a certain amount before any injury occurs. (This does not appear to be true (see § XII.4) of genetic damage.) If the dose exceeds the threshold, the damage may be reversible or irreversible; in the former case complete recovery of function is possible, whereas in the latter case the injury seems to be permanent.

The injury caused by radiation depends on the area (or volume) of the body that is exposed. In this connection a quantity called the *integral dose*, defined as the product of the dose and the mass of the body receiving that dose, is often used. When X rays or radioisotopes are used for diagnosis or treatment, limited portions of the body may receive large doses of radiation, but the integral dose is not excessive. This may result in considerable biological damage to the irradiated area, but the overall health of the individual is not seriously affected. The exposure of the whole body or a large portion of the body to the same total dose might be fatal, for the integral dose would be larger, and more sensitive tissue might be irradiated. For example, blood-forming and germ cells are very sensitive, whereas muscles are quite resistant to radiation-induced damage (or more readily repaired by the body).

Ultimately, the biological effects of nuclear radiation are largely attributed to ionization, which causes the destruction of various molecules that play an important part in the functioning of living cells. The production of biological damage starts with a physical act of absorption of energy whereby individual atoms are ionized and/or excited; the molecules of which they form a part become unstable. Usually the molecular configuration changes, and often the molecules break up. Since each living cell is a marvelously delicate balance of interacting materials, any chemical change in a cell, however slight, may have serious effects. It may substantially change the normal life processes, or even be lethal.

The extent of injury is determined by the amount of ionization produced (and hence by the energy absorbed), but the specific ionization has a considerable influence. In general, the greater the specific ionization, the greater the damage for a given absorption of energy.

Chronic local exposure of the skin, which is very sensitive to radiation, leads first to reddening (erythema), which may be followed by blistering and the formation of lesions that are very slow to heal compared with thermal burns. Loss of hair may also result from the action of radiations. Cancer of the skin may develop years after acute or chronic overexposure to ionising radiations.

There is considerable evidence, both from animal experiments and human mortality statistics, that exposure to moderate levels of radiation shortens life expectancy. (Radiologists die somewhat earlier on the average than physicians having no known contact with radiation.) The increased mortality rate is due not only to specific diseases, such as cancer and leukemia, but also to more general nonspecific effects.

A great deal of information of the consequences of acute overexposure to radiation has been accumulated from a study of Japanese victims of the nuclear bomb, as well as of a few persons who have suffered radiation accidents. The effects vary with the individual patient and the nature of the exposure. In any event, however, irradiation produces a variety of biological responses. These, in turn, lead to chains of secondary reactions. Primary and secondary effects are bound to interact with each other. The result is an intricate pattern that is far from being completely understood.

There are, as a rule, four phases in the response of the body to acute extreme overexposure to radiation. The early symptoms are nausea and vomiting, associated with a general lassitude. These symptoms are similar to those long known as being associated with "radiation sickness" suffered by patients undergoing intensive treatment with radium or X rays. This may be followed by a second phase of relative well-being, which may last for a few days or for several weeks; the more severe the radiation dose the shorter is this apparent latent period.

In the third phase the reaction of the body reaches its height, and the survival of the patient depends on the ability of his system to withstand the effects. Some of the symptoms are prostration, loss of appetite, loss of weight, fever, rapid heart action, severe diarrhea, bleeding of the gums, and loss of hair. This phase may last days or weeks, depending on the extent of the exposure. The patient may become progressively worse and succumb, or he may go through a period of prolonged convalescence in the fourth phase. During this time, which may last up to six months, there is gradual recovery.

Acute radiation sickness is accompanied by significant changes in the blood, the most obvious of which is a marked decrease in the number of white blood cells. Since the white cells are one of the most important defenses against bacteria, there is a greatly lowered resistance of the body to bacterial invasion and infection. The characteristic response of the healthy body to such invasion is inflammation, but in the body damaged by radiation this reaction is lost and death of tissue may result.

The influence of radiation on the blood is a manifestation of the fact that the lymphoid tissue (lymph nodes, spleen, tonsils, etc., which produce and store lymphocytes) and the bone marrow (which manufactures the granulocytes and platelets) are very sensitive and react quickly to irradiation. Other particularly sensitive tissues are the sex glands, the skin, the lining of the gastrointestinal tract, and the walls of the capillaries, which may be so weakened that hemorrhages occur throughout the body.

Although the manifestations of radiation damage may take some time to develop, the initial injury must occur at the time of exposure. In Table XII.3-1 are given estimates, based upon very limited data, of the early effects of whole-body exposure for average persons.

TABLE XII.3-1

PROBABLE EARLY EFFECTS OF ACUTE RADIATION
EXPOSURES OVER THE WHOLE BODY

Acute Dose (r)	Probable Effect
0-25	No detectable clinical effects.
25-50	Possible changes in blood and white matter of brain, but no other clinically detectable effects.
50-100	Nausea and fatigue; blood-cell changes; some injury, but no disability.
100-200	Nausea, vomiting, fatigue and reduced vitality; depression of nearly all blood elements. (Recovery in nearly all cases within 3-6 months.)
200-400	Same as above, with immediate disability; some deaths within 2-6 weeks.
400	Fatal to about 50%.
>600	Fatal to nearly all within 2 weeks.

XII.4. RADIATION AND GENETICS

Of the many problems accompanying the extensive use of atomic energy, as well as the widespread use of X radiation for medical and industrial purposes, the most insidious and potentially the most dangerous to man is that resulting from genetic damage leading to the production of mutations (hereditary changes). That this could occur was established by the work of Hermann J. Muller about thirty years ago, who studied the effects of ionizing radiations upon *Drosophila*, the fruit fly.

The formation of a new individual begins when the nuclei of an egg cell and a sperm cell fuse to form the one-celled zygote. The fertilized egg now has two sets of chromosomes, one from each of the parent cells. The two sets are equivalent (except for the chromosome concerned with sex), and thus there is a pair of each kind of chromosome.   In man, for example, each body cell contains twenty-three pairs of chromosomes, and each human egg and sperm contain one member of each of these pairs.   Before cell duplication (mitosis) each chromosome grows in size and then is duplicated lengthwise into two identical copies of the original. These copies separate during cell division, and the nuclei of each of the two daughter cells contain a complete set of chromosome pairs, one member of the pair inherited from the original egg and the other from the sperm.

The hereditary units, or genes, are carried on the chromosomes.   Taken together, these units determine all the potentialities of the individual: hair color, height, etc.   Since the chromosomes are paired, the genes are paired, one of each pair being inherited from the father and one from the mother.   Just which gene a

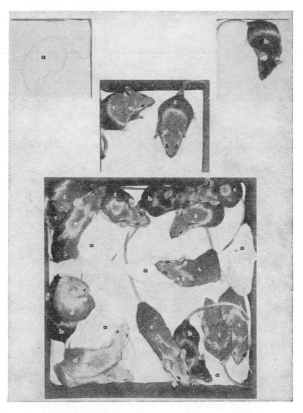

FIG. XII.4-1. *Effect of cross breeding on genetic variability as seen in coat colors. Inbred parent mice are seen at the top (a: albino strain; b: black strain). The first-generation hybrid is between them (c: black agouti). The second-generation hybrids are at the bottom and have five color types (d: brown agouti; e: brown). The numbers of each color type approximate the probability of occurrence as the ratio* 16: 27: 9: 9: 3 *for a, b, c, d, and e, respectively.*

child inherits from each of his mother's and father's gene pairs is a matter of chance. Thus the two genes in each pair are not necessarily, nor even usually, identical. If a child inherits a gene tending to produce red hair from his father, there is an excellent chance that the corresponding maternal gene will have some other color tendency. The actual color of hair in such a case is determined by the dominant gene. But the weaker or recessive gene is not completely submerged. In the example, the gene for red hair is recessive. The child who carries one such gene will have black, or brown or blond hair, but it will very likely have a rusty or tawny tinge. To make him a true redhead, both of the principal genes would have to be the type for red. The genetic effect of cross breeding as it affects the coat colors in mice is illustrated in Fig. XII.4-1.

Gene mutations, which result in altered characteristics, occur spontaneously, but the rate is very low. They can also be induced by heat, by certain chemicals, and by radiations. Once changed, the new form of the gene is passed on to daughter cells as faithfully as the old form was.

It is generally agreed that the vast majority of human mutations are disadvantageous, and that an increased number of mutations would result in more unfit persons. It is worth noting, however, that a minority of mutations may be desirable from a particular standpoint. Radiations were used to produce varieties of mold giving a higher yield of penicillin more rapidly than natural varieties. New strains of cereals that give better yields of grain in particular habitats have been produced by means of radiation.

Everyone is subjected to natural background radiation from radioactive elements in the earth and from cosmic rays. It has been proposed that this radiation is responsible for the so-called spontaneous mutations and that additional radiation causes further mutations and is thereby genetically harmful.

The change due to a mutated gene is seldom fully expressed in the first generation offspring of the person who received the radiation, because mutant genes are usually recessive. If a child gets from one parent a mutant gene, but from the other parent a normal gene belonging to that pair, then the normal gene is very likely to be at least partially dominant, so that the normal characteristic will appear. But, like the gene for red hair, the harmful recessive mutant genes are not usually completely masked and may still have a deleterious influence.

Most of the harm may remain unnoticed for a short or a long time in the genetic constitution of the successive generations of offspring. But the harm would persist, and some of it would be expressed in each generation. On the average, a detrimental mutation, no matter how small its harmful effect, will in the long run tip the scales against some descendant who carries this mutation, causing premature death or failure to produce the normal number of offspring. In this way harmful mutations are eventually eliminated from the population.

Each mutation is believed to be brought about by a single ionizing particle. If this is so, there is no minimum amount of radiation, no threshold, that must be exceeded before mutations occur. Any amount, however small, that reaches the reproductive cells could cause a correspondingly small number of mutations: the more radiation, the more mutations.   It is known that at least beyond a very small dose, the increase in the rate of mutation is roughly proportional to the amount of radiation to which the reproductive cells are exposed; if the radiation is increased by X per cent, then the number of mutations caused by the radiation will also increase by X per cent.   The total dose of radiation received by a person over his or her reproductive lifetime is what counts; the genetic damage caused by radiation is cumulative.

Injury to the genetic material of cells of many different types in the form of structural damage to the chromosomes can be seen under the microscope when the cell enters the first division after heavy irradiation.   Changes in pollen grains observed after low-intensity radiation showed:

Stickiness of chromosomes
Breakage of the centromere region (where the chromosomes are attached
    to the fibers of the spindle in the metaphase stage of cell division)
Errors in the formation of the spindle
Errors in spiralization (called spurious breakage)
Chromatid and chromosome breakage
Formation of nuclear fragments (micronuclei)

The first four are called physiological or temporary effects; they are manifested almost immediately and last only for a few hours after irradiation. They do not lead to any permanent modification of the chromosomes, but occasionally cause the death of the cell.

Structural changes are caused by the breakage of one or more chromosomes at two or more points, followed by the joining of the fragments at their broken ends, so as to form a new arrangement, that is, a new linear sequence of their component genes. Also the individual genes may themselves be changed, leading to "gene mutations." Since chromosomes carry the genes, permanent structural changes may result in genetical changes. Some of these forms of structural damage of the chromosomes are observed to increase in strict proportion to the dose over a certain range of dose. This is true of plant cells, insect embryos, mammalian tissues, and some kinds of cancer cells.

The sensitivity of chromosomes to breakage by X rays can be modified both by prior exposure to ionizing radiation and by exposure before or after irradiation to infrared light. This emphasizes that chromosome injuries are not the direct result of the passage of the ionizing particle, but are the result of a complex interplay of different factors in a living system which reacts to changes brought about in its environment. It is also possible that radiation causes the mutation of genes by some kind of direct action, perhaps by a hit on a large gene molecule.

Many chemicals can provoke lesions indistinguishable from those produced by radiation. Since the action of radiation in the cell is almost certainly indirect (i.e., produced by the free radicals formed), it is tempting to consider chromosome breakage purely as a physiological response to a biochemical disturbance. In any event, chromosomes are clearly not cut by radiation like grass with a scythe.

The main constituent (about 70 per cent) of most cells is water. Consequently when radiation passes through a cell, the water molecules are those most likely to be ionized, simply because of their predominance in terms of numbers. This suggests that the ionization of water may be one of the chief means by which radiation produces its effects on cells. Thus the ionized water produces free radicals, which may in turn inactivate enzymes, thereby starving the cell or causing other changes. Additional evidence for this arises from experiments in which H_2O_2, one of the products of the radiation ionization of water, was added to media in which bacteria were growing. Although the culture was not irradiated, mutant strains like those produced by radiation appeared after a short time.

A factor which argues strongly against a purely biochemical mechanism is that chromosome breakage is produced much more readily by radiation of high specific ionization. Thus, a dose of 5-Mev alpha particles may be 10 to 20 times as effective as a similar amount of energy delivered by X rays.

Radiant energy affects the progeny through alteration in the ovaries or testes of those irradiated, leading to sterility, primary changes in the sperms or eggs (making them incapable of fertilization), deaths of the fertilized eggs of foetuses *in utero*, etc. Such effects on mice have displayed a differential action on the fertility of the sexes; males can receive a higher dose than females and still remain fertile. Litter size is affected noticeably by irradiation, again the males showing less effect than the females.

Male mice exposed to an acute X-ray dose of a few hundred roentgens remain fertile for about 4-5 weeks. A period of sterility then sets in, after which fertility returns and is maintained. The temporary sterility is due to the depletion of spermatogonia (the primitive male germ cells), which are especially sensitive to killing by radiation. Fertility returns when adequate repopulation of spermatogonia has occurred.

Matings made during the presterile period utilize germ cells that were already in post-spermatogonial stages at the time of irradiation. The offspring in such cases show high incidences of effects (such as prenatal lethality, partial sterility, and sterility) that result primarily from major chromosomal aberrations.

An interesting use of the biological effects of irradiation was the eradication of the screwworm fly from the Dutch island of Curaçao in the West Indies. Male flies, reared in the laboratory and sterilized with gamma rays from Co^{60}, were released in the field to compete for mates with normal males. It was possible to release sterile insects in greater numbers than existed in nature. Although males may mate repeatedly, the females mate only once; those that mated with sterile mates were incapable of reproduction. The sterile males competed so effectively that screwworms were eradicated.

XII.5. RADIOISOTOPES AND MEDICINE

The discovery and wide availability of radioactive tracers have led to many significant advances in medicine. These substances have proved extremely useful in the field of research and for diagnostic and therapeutic purposes.

The therapeutic uses of radioactive isotopes are based on the observation that any ionizing radiation will, if sufficiently intense, kill all living cells exposed to it. During the process of growth the susceptibility of cells to radiation is greater than when they are in the fully developed stage. In cancerous tissues the abnormal cells are undergoing rapid growth so that by using just the right dosage there exists the possibility that such cells may be eliminated without seriously damaging the normal cells. The ability of some radioactive emitters to localize and concentrate in certain tissues offers a very real advantage over the use of any source of external radiation, since in this way the irradiation of normal tissue is reduced. In general, therapeutic applications have been limited by the need for sharp localization of the material administered in the tissue to be treated, by the sensitivity of the tissue to radiation, and by the level of the radiation given to the remainder of the body.

Cobalt-60 has been widely used as an external source of radiation, often as a convenient substitute for radium in multicurie quantities. To a lesser extent, cobalt-60 has been used in the form of interstitial therapy as needles or beads. The chief advantages of radiocobalt are its availability in large quantities at low dose and its very high specific activity. The characteristics of its radiations, however, are not such as to give significant qualitative advantages over radium or supervoltage X rays.

Strontium-90 provides a useful external source of fairly intense beta emission for superficial therapy, penetrating up to 3 mm of tissue. Radioactive thulium, with the equivalent of 85-kv radiation and a 129-day half-life, has been utilized as the equivalent of an X-ray generator and has potentialities for portable diagnostic use.

The advantage of radioisotopes for diagnostic purposes lies in the fact that only very small amounts of the material are needed. One example of such an application is provided by the employment of radioactive sodium to diagnose cases of restricted circulation of the blood. A small quantity of sodium chloride solution, in which the sodium has been labeled with sodium-24, is injected into a vein of the patient's forearm. If the blood circulation is normal, the presence of radioactivity is very soon detected, by means of, say, a G-M counter, in the foot. Usually, the activity increases rapidly and reaches a maximum value within less than an hour. If there is a circulatory impairment of some kind, however, the radioactivity may increase but slowly, indicating that the blood has difficulty in reaching the foot. By moving the counter to different parts of the body the position of any restriction can be located.

Most medical applications of radioisotopes, both diagnostic and therapeutic, depend on the property of being preferentially absorbed at certain locations. A relatively small preferential uptake is generally adequate for diagnosis, but satisfactory therapy requires considerable radioactivity to be concentrated in the tissues or organs to be treated. It is necessary, therefore, that the latter should exhibit marked preferential absorption of the radioelement in order that administration of dangerous quantities of radioactive material to the body as a whole may be avoided.

Iodine, which is rapidly taken up by the thyroid gland (as well as by the liver, spleen, and heart), provides an example of a radioisotope that has been used since 1942 both for diagnosis and for therapy. The thyroid gland, which has the function of regulating metabolism, is a small gland surrounding the windpipe in the throat. The uptake of iodine-131 (8-day half-life; a fission product of uranium, resulting from the beta decay of 30-minute tellurium-131) is a highly accurate key to the metabolic activity of the thyroid. (The first step in the production of the thyroid hormone consists of the fixation of iodine.) Iodine is taken up by the thyroid at such a rapid rate that if a few milligrams of stable iodine tagged with radioactive iodine are injected into a vein, less than half an hour is needed for approximately one-half of the iodine to be concentrated in the gland.

In the case of hyperthyroidism the thyroid gland is overactive, and the condition can be readily demonstrated and diagnosed following the oral administration of small quantities of sodium iodide containing some radioiodine. The gamma radiations emitted by the radioiodine act like X rays in causing a partial destruction of the thyroid gland and hence its return to a more normal level of physiological activity.

It is generally claimed that the results of this procedure are at least as good as are obtained by surgical treatment. Advantages of this method include the fact that no surgery is involved, thereby avoiding any risks from the use of anesthesia; there is no pain nor discomfort as a result of the treatment; no hospitalization is required. Further, there is no damage of the parathyroid gland and no recurrent nerve damage. Disadvantages of the method include the observation that there is a latent period (which may last as long as two months) before the activity subsides. One of the chief problems involved in the treatment of hyperthyroidism with radioactive iodine is to estimate the proper dose, since it is difficult to estimate the size or mass of the gland, generally accomplished by feel. It is extremely difficult to predict accurately the amount of radiation that any given area of thyroid tissue will receive, nor can it be ascertained how uniformly the thyroid will take up iodine-131. Too small a dose is insufficient to effect a cure, while too large a dose may lead to hypothyroidism. Accordingly, instead of giving a single dose, there is a general trend to the administration of small and repeated doses to avoid such post-therapeutic hypothyroidism. The use of adequate doses may prove to be carcinogenic, although no proved malignancies have been found in people treated with therapeutic doses of iodine-131; nonetheless, such cancers have been induced in animal experiments.

At one time radioiodine was heralded as a possible panacea for treatment of carcinoma of the thyroid that was not amenable to surgery. The treatment has proved beneficial in some, but not all, types of cancer of the thyroid gland. In order to obtain a beneficial response from iodine-131, the cancer cell must have an affinity for the isotope and concentrate it as does a normal thyroid cell. Not all carcinomas of the thyroid have an avidity for iodine-131, however. If no uptake is found in a given case, as determined by the use of iodine tracer, then treatment with iodine-131 is not warranted. Unfortunately, it appears that the most malignant thyroid cancers do not concentrate iodine-131.

In some cases hypothyroidism has been deliberately induced by iodine-131 to lessen the work of the heart. The benefits gained are a result of the lowering of the metabolic rate, which reduces systemic circulatory requirements so as to place them within the limit of the cardiac reserve. The treatment is a palliative, however, and not to be considered as curative.

An exceptionally interesting diagnostic application of radioiostopes has been made in the study of brain tumors. The positions of such tumors are not only difficult to determine, but, once located, the tumorous mass is not readily distinguishable from the normal tissue. In this connection use has been made of the fact that fluorescein, a dye, and related compounds, such as tetraiodophenol-phthalein, are taken up preferentially by the tumor. Hence, after injection of a derivative of this dye containing radioiodine, the tumor can be located by means of an external counter, because the gamma rays can penetrate the skull and be detected outside the head. However, the long range of these radiations makes it almost impossible to determine the limits of the tumor. This can be done by use of a simple compound containing phosphorus-32, which is a pure beta emitter of short half-life, and which is also preferentially absorbed by the tumor. Further, during the surgical operation for excision of the tumor the extent of the affected tissue can be made evident by means of a detector for the short-range beta particles (2-mm mean path in tissue).

Radiophosphorus has also found application in the treatment of two diseases of the blood, both of which are usually fatal; these are leukemia, which is an overproduction of the white corpuscles (leucocytes) of the blood, and polycy-themia vera, characterized by an excess of red cells. Both types of blood cor-puscles are formed in the bone marrow, which, incidentally, exhibits preferential absorption of phosphorus to a small extent. The oral ingestion of radioactive phosphorus has, therefore, been used with some success, particularly in the treatment of polycythemia vera. The beta radiations emitted by phosphorus-32 which has concentrated in the bone marrow inhibit the excessive formation of the red blood cells. Remissions as long as five years have been observed following single doses of phosphorus-32.

Gold-198, made by the $Au^{197}(n,\gamma)Au^{198}$ reaction, is physiologically inert and does not set up a foreign-body reaction when administered in colloidal form. Gold-198 has a half-life of 2.7 days and possesses a mixed spectrum of an 0.96-Mev beta particle (about 90 to 95 per cent) and a 0.45-Mev gamma. The application of radioactive colloidal gold (doses of 50 to 250 mc) by introduction into the peritoneal and pleural cavities has been used to control effusions due to secondary carcinomatosis. The colloid is deposited, usually unevenly, on the surfaces of the cavity. The beta particle emitted has a mean path of only about 0.7 mm. This short mean path has also made radiogold colloids useful in the treatment of other surface lesions.

When injected into tumors or normal tissues, colloids tend to stay at or near the site of injection. This is presumed to be due to adherence of the substance to cells and intercellular material without the presence of any very active or dynamic physiological processes. Such localization makes it possible to deliver very high doses to tumors themselves while subjecting surrounding tissues to low doses, if uniformity of distribution of the colloidal material can be accomplished. In contrast to the implanting of discrete sources of radium or other radioisotopes, the directly injected colloid requires no subsequent removal.

Interstitial infiltrations of radioactive colloidal gold in and around otherwise untreatable malignant tumors has been employed. Such an example is unoperable carcinoma of the prostate gland. Ordinarily the doses used vary from 1 to 3 mc per estimated cubic centimeter of tumor.

Normal physiologic processes are also being studied with radioactive isotopes of iron, phosphorus, chromium, potassium, and thorium at trace levels. For example, it is possible to measure the total circulating red-cell volume of the blood with accuracy and ease, because the isotopes may be incorporated into the red cells *in vitro*. This permits the labeling of an individual's own red cells. Iron, on the other hand, must first be administered to a donor, whose red cells are subsequently injected into an individual whose blood volume is to be determined.

Iron-59 (a beta-gamma emitter with a half-life of 46 days) has been used for the direct determination of the rate of production of red cells. This is accomplished by measuring the rate of disappearance of radioactive iron from the plasma and the subsequent uptake of radioiron in the red cells. In general it has been found that 0.26 mg of iron is utilized for red-cell production per kilogram per day in a normal male. Much higher values are found in cases of polycythemia. In leukemia these values are normal or are found to be increased to two to three times normal. Radioiron has also been useful in determining the metabolism of iron in the body.

In medical research the outstanding advance of radioactive tracers is the fact that amounts so minute as to have no toxic effect nor any significant alteration of normal physiological or biochemical processes can be used to follow vital processes in detail, both in space and in time. These tracers follow the same metabolic pathways as do their normal counterparts among the elements. Their specific radioactivities may be made so high that they can be readily identified.

Gold-198 has a half-life of 2.7 days and possesses a mixed spectrum of an 0.96-Mev

XII.6. RADIOISOTOPES AND BIOLOGICAL STUDIES

It is now about 35 years since Hevesy introduced a radioactive isotope as an indicator in plant studies. He used thorium B (Pb^{212}) in a study of the uptake of lead by plants. Since that time, and particularly since 1945, when many different isotopes became readily available for widespread use, isotopic tracers have been widely employed for biological studies, giving the scientist means of following processes in living things in a way previously impossible.

Prior to 1938 it had been universally believed that degradative changes in the living animal took place slowly, the purpose of food being largely to supply the currently required energy, while a small proportion went to replace worn-out tissue. As a result of experiments carried out since 1938 by R. Schoenheimer, D. Rittenberg and their associates, who used deuterium and stable nitrogen-15 as tracers, this long-established concept of an essentially static or dormant state of the organism has been shown to be entirely wrong. Rather, the body constituents are in a dynamic state, in which there is a continual interchange between the fats, proteins, and carbohydrates already present in the animal body with those ingested in the form of food.

Linseed oil, which contains fats with double and triple bonds, was partially deuterated to yield a mixture of both saturated (no double bonds) and slightly unsaturated fats. In the process two or four of the hydrogen atoms attached to the carbon were replaced by deuterium. When such linseed oil was fed to animals, only a small proportion of the deuterium was excreted during several days. The major portion of the deuterium was found to have been deposited in the fatty portions of the body. Even when the diet was very deficient in fat, and the total supply of calories was inadequate, so that the animal was drawing on its reserves, the deutero-fat was mainly stored and not put to immediate use, as might have been expected.

After the natural diet of the animals had been resumed, the labeled fats were found to disappear gradually, and the deuterium left the body in the form of water. However, if the water in the normal diet was enriched in heavy water, so as to maintain a constant level of deuterium in the body fluids, the stored fat was found to gain deuterium at the same rate as it had been lost when animals were removed from a diet of deutero-fats. These results indicate that a reversible, dynamical equilibrium involving fats and water exists in the living organism.

Schoenheimer and Rittenberg prepared a number of amino acids in which the nitrogen of the amino group, $-NH_2$, was labeled with the stable nitrogen-15 isotope. When fed to animals, it was found that nearly all the amino acids isolated from tissue protein contained nitrogen-15; further, the concentration of the isotope was greatest in the amino acid corresponding to that which had been labeled in the diet. It would thus appear (1) that the dietary amino acid is taken up directly and rapidly into the body protein and (2) that there is a biological transfer of nitrogen from one protein amino acid to another during metabolism.

Another example of the use of isotopes as a tool is offered by studies of photosynthesis, the basic characteristics of which were discovered in the period between 1770 and 1800. In sunlight, green plants can take up CO_2 and H_2O, which they convert into the complex, energy-containing carbohydrates — sugars, starches, and celluloses; at the same time they liberate oxygen. There is no doubt that the processes involved are very complicated, requiring several intermediate stages, but the overall action may be represented approximately by

$$xCO_2 + yH_2O + \text{energy } h\nu \xrightarrow{\text{chlorophyll}} C_xH_{2y}O_y + xO_2,$$

where $C_xH_{2y}O_y$ is the general formula for a carbohydrate and the energy is that of sunlight. Note that in the absence of chlorophyll, or possibly some equivalent substance, photosynthesis cannot occur.

CO_2 and H_2O each contain oxygen. Does the liberated oxygen originate from the CO_2 or from the H_2O, or from both? Using CO_2 and H_2O containing oxygen-18, Ruben and Kamen have shown that all the oxygen liberated in photosynthesis originates in the H_2O; none comes from the CO_2. This is consistent with the hypothesis that photosynthesis is fundamentally a transfer of hydrogen atoms from H_2O to CO_2, with the oxygen left behind.

The study of the intermediate stages of photosynthesis presented a virtually insuperable problem until the advent of isotopes as a tool opened up new possibilities. Some preliminary observations were made in 1940 with the short-lived carbon-11 (a half-life of 21 minutes), but the quantity obtained by cyclotron bombardment was very small, and its rapid decay made experimentation difficult. Since then radioactive 5360-year carbon-14, made by the reaction $N^{14}(n,p)C^{14}$, has become available at reasonable prices. It has been found that CO_2 unites reversibly in a nonphotochemical reaction (for the CO_2 is taken up in the dark) with a heavy molecule of the type RH, where R is an atomic aggregate of large total weight:

$$RH + CO_2 \rightleftarrows RCOOH.$$

The RCOOH molecule unites photochemically with H_2O to form a possible sugar:

$$RCOOH + H_2O + h\nu \rightarrow RCH_2OH + O_2.$$

In Russia, with the use of carbon-14 in the form of CO_2 and nitrogen-15 in the form of an ammonium salt, it has been demonstrated that not only carbohydrates but proteins as well are the direct products of photosynthesis in the leaves of plants. Carbohydrates are synthesized mainly in the red and yellow part of the spectrum, while proteins are formed under the influence of blue light.

The usefulness of any tracer isotope is limited by factors other than its availability in elemental form. The most limiting factor in applying carbon-14 as a tracer in biological research is the requirement of incorporating it into the molecules of the particular native organic compound that is to be traced or studied. In many cases this incorporation can be most efficiently accomplished by means of chemical synthesis, in which case it is possible to place the isotope at specific carbon atom positions. In many more cases the mechanism of synthesis of naturally occurring organic compounds is not known and the preparation of a labeled molecule cannot be accomplished. It is only by use of biosynthesis that a radiocarbon-tagged form of all the diverse organic molecules that occur in living organisms can be prepared.

In biosynthesis an actively metabolizing organism is supplied the carbon-containing substrates or "assimilates" normally utilized in its natural habitat. These substrates are supplied in carbon-14-enriched forms.

EXPERIMENTS

EXPERIMENTS IN NUCLEAR SCIENCE*

RATIO OF CHARGE TO MASS

In this experiment a simple apparatus for the measurement of the ratio of the charge carried by an ion to its mass is assembled. This is basically what most mass spectrometers do and in this sense the apparatus you are to work with is a mass spectrometer. Because of the extreme experimental difficulty involved in measuring massive charged particles, this apparatus is most easily used for electrons.

As part of the assembly there is a glass-to-metal seal, with two or four wires running through the glass. To two of the wires there is attached a small tungsten ribbon which serves as a hot filament for the generation of electrons.

A second part of the apparatus consists of a flat strip of metal with a clamp at one end and a small slot toward the middle; a fluorescent material has been sprayed on one side. This is called the base plate. In the final assembly this strip is to be clamped around the metal tube holding the tungsten ribbon and electrical leads with the ribbon just below the slot.

When the apparatus is operating, a source of current is connected to the two leads of the filament to heat it. Usually between 2 and 5 volts at up to 5 amp is needed. A source of much higher voltage (depending upon the magnetic field available) is connected between the filament and the metal strip, the filament being connected to the negative side of this high-voltage source. Very small current capacities are needed in the high voltage since only currents of the order of fractions of a milliampere are involved. A magnetic field must be established with the field direction at right angles to the length of and parallel to the plane of the metal strip. This field should be approximately uniform over a circular area preferably 3 or 4 inches in diameter.

*Oak Ridge National Laboratory has distributed radioisotopes for educational purposes to those licensed by the United States Atomic Energy Commission. A prospective user should write to

>Isotopes Branch
>Division of Licensing and Regulation
>U. S. Atomic Energy Commission
>Washington 25, D. C.

to inform them of his needs and qualifications for handling radioactive material. Purchase orders should be directed to:

>Union Carbide Nuclear Co.
>Oak Ridge National Laboratory
>Isotope Sales Dept.
>P. O. Box X
>Oak Ridge, Tennessee

The proper operation of the apparatus requires an interrelationship between the voltage applied between the filament and the metal strip and the magnetic field. When the filament is hot, electrons escape from the tungsten surface and are immediately attracted toward the base plate. Most of them strike the strip

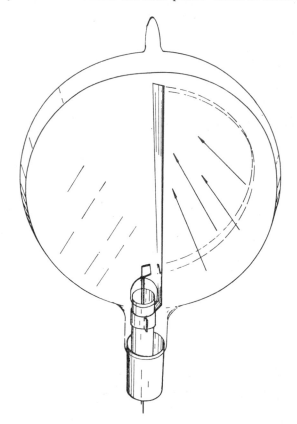

Fig. E-1. *Assembled apparatus for measurement of ratio of charge to mass for electrons.*

and are lost; however, a tiny fraction is so directed that they pass through the slot. As a result of the attraction to the base plate, the electrons pick up velocity; when they pass through the slot they keep this velocity, since there are no voltages on that side of the base plate. However, the moving charges are affected by the magnetic field, which causes them to move in approximately a semicircular path until they collide with the phosphor on the base plate, where their energy is converted into light. Consequently, when the apparatus is operating properly, a line will appear on the base plate at the end away from the slot. Its position will depend upon the initial accelerating voltage (the voltage between the filament and base plate) and the strength of the magnetic field which crosses the region within which the electrons are moving. In the usual mass spectrometer the charges are not electrons, but are ions of atoms or molecules which are several thousand times heavier; the principle is exactly the same, however.

The motions of ions under these circumstances have been studied in great detail and we may summarize this by the mathematical relation:

$$e/m = 3230V/B^2r^2,$$

where

V = voltage between the filament and base plate;

B = strength of the magnetic field;

r = radius of the path (one-half of the distance between the slot and spot); and

e/m = ratio of the charge carried by the ion to its mass.

Visually, the diameter of the ion path may be measured by means of lines scratched at half-inch intervals on the base plate. Upon measurement of the magnetic field and the voltage, it is then possible to calculate the quantity e/m for the ion. For electrons this turns out to be 1.8×10^8 emu/gm. Unfortunately, there is only one electronic mass and so only a single spot appears on the fluorescent screen. If, however, ions of atoms or molecules are used, as in a mass spectrometer, a number of separate spots corresponding to various masses would appear on the fluorescent screen as separate spots. It is this property of separating masses which has made the mass spectrometer so valuable in studying such things as isotopic content in the elements, the precise measurement of their masses, and kindred subjects in the field of nuclear energy. Such instruments have also been used and are being used in the actual physical separation of large quantities of isotopes at Oak Ridge, Tennessee.

The final operation of the assembly is to insert the filament-base plate subassembly into the flask. This must then be sealed so as to be vacuum tight after the residual gas is removed as completely as possible. A vacuum is necessary so that the electrons or other types of ions may proceed from the filament through the slot and to the screen without being scattered by collisions. However, since the mere fact of pumping the system to remove this air from the paths of the ions seems to have little pedagogical value, this operation will be done by the Laboratory.

MAGNETIC FIELD ASSEMBLY FOR e/m APPARATUS

The magnetic field arrangement used in the demonstration of the e/m apparatus does not represent a particularly good design but is included to form a basis for the construction of other units adapted to material at hand and the power supplies available.

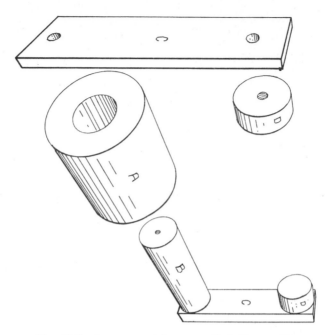

FIG. E-2. *Arrangement for magnetic field assembly.*

In the apparatus used during the course, the magnet coil shown at A in Fig. E-2 had 20,000 turns of very fine copper wire and was excited with about $\frac{1}{3}$ amp of direct current. This gave an mmf of 6000 ampere turns, approximately, as a reasonable upper limit when 1500 volts of electron acceleration were used. If low voltage sources of power are used, 5000 or 6000 ampere turns are still needed, but the number of turns of wire is reduced.

The internal diameter of the coil is 3 in., which was loosely fitted with a 3-in. bar of ordinary steel, shown in B. Two flat plates of steel, about $\frac{1}{2}$ in. thick and 3 in. wide, shown in C, were bolted to this. Finally, two pole pieces, also 3 in. in diameter of ordinary steel, which enclose the e/m tube, were bolted to the side plates (shown in D). The gap between the pole faces was big enough to accommodate the glass enclosure. The diameter of the pole pieces in the demonstration model was 5 in., but this did not seem to substantially improve the performance of the apparatus.

CAUTION: With the magnet assembled and the coil excited, the resulting magnetic field can be detrimental to watches.

NOTES FOR A HIGH-VOLTAGE POWER SUPPLY

A suitable high-voltage power supply is a necessary adjunct to setting up demonstrations of the use of Geiger counters, proportional counters, and similar detectors of nuclear radiations. The proper connection of such a supply to various detectors is shown in Figs. E-3, E-4, E-5, and E-6.

One of the most familiar detectors is the Geiger-Müller or G-M tube used in portable Geiger counters. Fig. E-3 shows the connection of such a tube to the

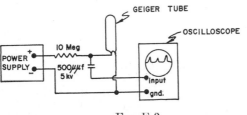

FIG. E-3.

power supply and to an oscilloscope for viewing the pulses. If no oscilloscope is available, the pulses may be heard as audible clicks in sensitive crystal earphones, or through a small audio amplifier and speaker, as in Figs. E-4 and E-5. The

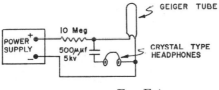

FIG. E-4.

sensitivity will be sufficient to detect easily the radiation from the face of a luminous watch dial. It should be noted that the G-M tube can be permanently damaged by operating it at voltages higher than those for which it is rated. A

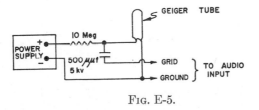

FIG. E-5.

suitable meter should be used with the power supply to permit setting the correct voltage. A suitable G-M tube is the Victoreen 1 B85, which may be purchased from Allied Radio Corporation, Chicago, for $8.50. This tube operates at 900 volts.

Fig. E-6 shows the proper connections for a proportional counter, such as the one described in "Sewing-Needle Proportional Counter" by A. H. Benade and R. E. Chrien of Case Institute of Technology.[1] In this case the required operating

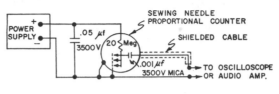

FIG. E-6.

voltage is about 2600 volts. The high-voltage supply has been substituted for the switch, ignition coil, and spark-gap arrangement described in the above paper.

It is also possible to utilize this supply for operation of a multiplier phototube for use as a scintillation counter. The RCA type 931-A ($10.50) is an inexpensive

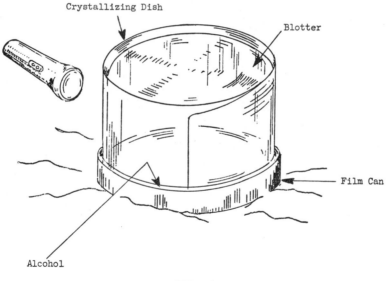

FIG. E-7. *Simple diffusion cloud chamber.*

tube for this purpose. It must be remembered that, for scintillation counting, the "window," or light-sensitive area, of the phototube must be in intimate physical contact with the scintillating material, and both phototube and scintillator must, of course, be in a light-tight enclosure. Since the 931-A has its light-sensitive area on the cylindrical side of the glass tube, the scintillator must be made

[1] A. H. Benade and R. E. Chrien, *American Journal of Physics* 25: 313-317 (May 1957).

concave to fit against this part of the tube. Therefore, a plastic scintillator material would be best suited, since it can easily be machined to this shape, and the concave surface polished. Plastic scintillators are relatively inexpensive, the cost being only a few dollars per pound. A complete description of the setup required for a suitable scintillation counter is beyond the scope of these notes, but detailed information concerning the 931-A multiplier phototube may be secured from RCA, Electron Tube Division. Information on plastic scintillators may be obtained from Crystals, Incorporated, 123 Woodland Avenue, Westwood, New Jersey.

DIFFUSION CLOUD CHAMBER

When a warm vapor is allowed to fall through cold gas, a condition of super-saturation may be achieved. When this happens, the vapor can condense on ions, giving rise to visible droplets.

Our diffusion cloud chamber works with alcohol and air. The metal bottom of the chamber sits on dry ice, while the top is exposed to room air. The capillary action of a blotter causes alcohol to rise to the top of the chamber, where it evaporates and falls to form a region of supersaturated gas-vapor mixture.

A flashlight is used to make visible the paths of ionizing particles which pass through the sensitive region of the chamber.

ELECTROSCOPE

Previous to the dropping of the first A-bomb, probably more nuclear research data had been turned out with the gold-leaf electroscope than with any other instrument.

The electroscope consists of an insulated conductor, a part of which is a light flexible member, such as a piece of gold leaf. When the conductor is charged, the flexible member will be repelled by the rest of the conductor and it can be made to assume an equilibrium position under the effects of electrostatic and gravitational forces. With a change in amount of charge, a change in the position of the flexible member will occur. The charge can be reduced if ions are produced near the leaf. It is the ionization caused by radiation which is measured by the rate of change of the position of the leaf.

The electroscope is generally used for relative measurements of radiations of the same type. It does not have a linear scale, and therefore timing should be carried out over the same positions of the gold leaf.

CONSTRUCTION

There are various types of gold-leaf electroscopes, each suited to a specific purpose. The electroscope to be described has a separate ionization chamber and is constructed of materials which happened to be available.

The inside of a two-ounce, square bottle with a medium-sized mouth is coated with Aquadag, except for areas on two opposite sides, which are to serve as windows. This will serve as the chamber for the gold leaf.

The coating is brought up over the rim of the neck and down the outside, so that electrical contact can be made with the screw cap. If the cap is a good insulator (polystyrene or some polyethylenes), the conductor may be a piece of No. 12 bare copper wire flattened at the end to which the gold leaf is to be attached and formed as shown in Fig. E-8. After the conductor has been shaped

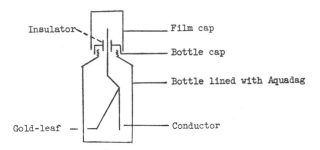

FIG. E-8. *Arrangement of the electroscope.*

and fastened through the screw top, the threads inside the cap are made conducting with Aquadag or conducting paint, and the coating is carried to the outside of the cap. Care must be taken to keep the conductor insulated.

The gold leaf, actually metal leaf as used by sign painters, is cut to size between two sheets of paper, the cutting being done with a razor blade guided by a ruler. A strip about $\frac{3}{32}$ inch wide and 1 inch long is suitable for this construction. The gold leaf may be fastened to the conductor with Aquadag, conducting paint, glue, Vaseline, or even a mixture of sweat and oil from the skin.

The ionization chamber is formed by slipping a thin aluminum 35-mm film can onto the bottlecap.

STRONTIUM BEAD SOURCES

The source consists of a small bead of glass which formed from powdered glass upon which Sr^{90} has been absorbed. This bead is imbedded in a piece of Lucite of a size and shape suitable for safe handling and usefulness in experimental work. Further safety in transportation and storage is obtained with the lead shield.

A small, intensely radioactive but chemically inert source has many experimental uses. Originally the glass bead was designed for implantation in living tissue, but it was also found useful in surface irradiations — for example, in a study of the effects of irradiation on the circulation of blood in the bat wing. This suggested its use as a teaching aid for demonstrating biological effects of radiation. The holder and shield were designed to make the unit quite versatile and reasonably safe. The size of the Lucite holder permits handling of the source with comparative safety. The holder is flat and transparent so that it may be used with a microscope. For example, amebas or other protozoa could be placed in a drop of water over the bead and observed for radiation effects. Onion or other root tips growing in a moist chamber could be exposed to the radiation from the source, etc.

Unfortunately, the amount of radiation necessary to demonstrate radiation effects is about 25 to 50 times that which the Atomic Energy Commission permits to be released without license. The sources contain less than 1 microcurie of Sr^{90} in equilibrium with Y^{90}, but are useful for a number of experiments nevertheless.

SAFETY SUGGESTIONS FOR THE USE OF Sr^{90} SOURCES

The strontium sources to be used contain approximately 1 microcurie of Sr^{90} in equilibrium with Y^{90}. After allowing for the absorption in the source holder, the radiation is emitted from the unshielded source at a rate of about fifteen (15) millirep per hour at a distance of 2 inches. This dose rate will vary roughly with the inverse square of the distance.

The total dose from this type of radiation to the most sensitive parts of the body should not exceed thirty (30) millirep in any one week. This dose would be received by any part of the body within 2 inches of the source for a total period of 2 hours.

Precautions should be exercised when using the source to keep exposures at a minimum. Keep the source shielded at all times when not in use. When the source is unshielded, try not to expose any part of the body directly to the radiation. This type of radiation will not pass through any material which has a thickness greater than 1.2 gm per square centimeter. This corresponds to a thickness of about 1 mm of lead. The source should be used behind a shielding material if possible when the user must be continually near it.

SUGGESTED EXPERIMENTS

1. Determine and record the strength of the source.
2. Study the absorption of beta particles.
3. Study the inverse-square law.
4. Observe fluorescence of zinc sulfide or other phosphor.
5. Make a betagraph. Use the source as a small "X ray" machine to make radiographs of insects, leaves, etc.

The shield was made larger than really necessary so that a collimating hole of desired size could be bored near one end or so that other modifications, as yet unforeseen, might be made.

DEMONSTRATION OF RADIOACTIVE DECAY

In this experiment the decay of 30-second Rh^{106} is observed and the half-life determined from a semilogarithmic plot of the decay data. The isotope Rh^{106} arises from the decay of 1.0-year Ru^{106}, which is formed as a product of nuclear fission. The fission decay chain may be written as

$$\text{1.0-year } Ru^{106} \xrightarrow{\beta^-} \text{30-second } Rh^{106} \xrightarrow{\beta^-} \text{stable } Pd^{106}.$$

This may be recognized as a case of secular equilibrium, since $\lambda_1 \ll \lambda_2$. The radiations of Ru^{106} are extremely weak and are easily stopped by the glass walls of a containing vessel. Those of Rh^{106}, on the other hand, are very energetic, and in the equilibrium mixture only the activity of the Rh^{106} is generally observed.

A source of Ru^{106}-Rh^{106} is obtainable from the Oak Ridge National Laboratory Radioisotopes Division as a solution of the chlorides. The oxide RuO_4 is distilled from the source by oxidation with $KMnO_4$-H_2SO_4 solution, and the distillate is trapped in a solution of 1 N H_2SO_4 containing SO_2. Aliquots of the distillate are removed for the preparation of the demonstration solutions.

The radioactive aliquots are added to a solution which is 1 N in H_2SO_4, 0.5 M in $Ce(HSO_4)_4$, and 0.1 M in $K_2S_2O_8$. An equal volume of CCl_4 is added to the aqueous solution and the vessel sealed. In this solution, Ru is oxidized to RuO_4 and may be extracted into the CCl_4 phase, leaving the Rh in the aqueous phase. Since the latter is left unsupported by its parent, it will decay with its own 30-second half-life. In the CCl_4 phase, the Ru will again grow more 30-second Rh, equilibrium being reached in a few minutes. The CCl_4 phase now acts as an essentially constant source of activity from which the 30-second Rh^{106} may be extracted at will into the aqueous phase, and its decay may be followed. It is also possible to follow the growth of Rh^{106} back into the CCl_4 phase, but owing to the relatively long time for phase separation, only the latter stages of growth are usually observed by this method.

EQUIPMENT

The apparatus necessary for this experiment consists of the Ru-Rh source, a detector (Geiger-Müller tube), counting-rate meter, shield with hole permitting observation of either phase without interference from the other (see Fig. E-9), and timer.

PROCEDURE

1. Shake the cylinder containing the Ru-Rh mixture vigorously for about 5-10 seconds. Allow a few seconds for phase separation in the uppermost part of the aqueous (top) phase, and quickly adjust the position of the cylinder opposite the hole in the shield.

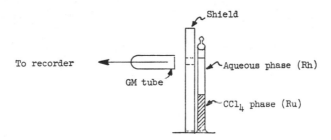

FIG. E-9. *Schematic of apparatus arrangement.*

2. Record the activity indicated on the meter at 10-second intervals for a few minutes.

3. After about 4-5 minutes, observe the steady background activity being recorded on the meter.

4. Subtract the background activity from each of the observed points and plot the net activity on semilogarithmic paper as a function of time.

5. From the best straight line through the data, obtain the half-life of Rh^{106}.

URANYL OXALATE ACTINOMETER

In radiation chemical studies it is very important to know the total amount of irradiation (or dose) being absorbed by the sample being studied. For example, the ferrous sulfate reaction (discussed in the lecture) is widely used in measuring the dose absorbed in aqueous solutions being exposed to gamma rays from Co^{60}. This reaction has been carefully standardized by measuring the heat absorbed by a solution of ferrous sulfate, calorimetrically, and simultaneously measuring chemically the amount of ferrous ion oxidized by the same dose. From the calorimetric determination, one calculates the energy in electron volts absorbed by the solution and from the chemical determination the number of ferrous ions oxidized to ferric ions. Using these two determinations, the number of ferrous ions oxidized per unit energy absorbed is calculated. This is expressed by a quantity called G, which is the number of ferrous ions oxidized per 100 electron volts of energy absorbed. The value of G accepted for the ferrous sulfate dosimeter is 15.5 ferrous ions oxidized per 100 ev absorbed.

In photochemistry a similar method is used to express the yield of a photochemical reaction. The quantity used here is Φ, the quantum yield, which expresses the number of molecules reacting per quantum of light energy being absorbed. Here, again, chemical dosimeters are used. The amount of chemical reaction induced by a given amount of light of a particular wavelength is measured. Simultaneously, the energy absorbed is measured by the emf generated when a standard thermopile absorbs the same dose of light of the given wavelength, giving the number of photons absorbed by the thermopile. From these measurements the yield or number of molecules reacting per photon absorbed by the actinometer, Φ, is calculated. Knowing this value of Φ, one can measure the number of photons entering other chemical systems by replacing the solution being studied by the actinometer solution and measuring the amount of chemical change occurring.

A very widely used chemical actinometer used in photochemical studies in the region from 4400 Å to 2000 Å is the uranyl oxalate actinometer. This consists of a solution of uranyl oxalate and oxalic acid. The uranyl ion absorbs the light and transfers it to the oxalate ion, which then decomposes according to the equation

$$H_2C_2O_4 \rightarrow H_2O + CO_2 + CO.$$

This is known as a photosensitized decomposition, the uranyl ion photosensitizing the decomposition of the oxalic acid. The quantum yield Φ for this reaction for different wavelengths is given in Table E-1. If one measures the oxalic acid

TABLE E-I

QUANTUM YIELDS AT DIFFERENT WAVELENGTHS

Wavelength, Å	Quantum Yield	Wavelength, Å	Quantum Yield
4350	0.58	3020	0.57
4050	0.56	2780	0.58
3660	0.49	2650	0.58
3350	0.53	2540	0.64-0.60
3130	0.56	2080	0.47-0.50

before and after exposure to the light for a given length of time, one can, using the known value of Φ, calculate the number of photons being absorbed by the actinometer and therefore by the reaction cell, after making sure that absorption is practically complete in both cases.

EXPERIMENTAL

Chemical Reagents. A solution containing approximately 0.01 M uranyl oxalate and 0.05 M oxalic acid is furnished. If one wishes to prepare this solution the following procedure is used. The uranyl oxalate may be prepared by mixing a hot solution of uranyl sulfate and recrystallized oxalic acid and allowing the solution to cool and the precipitated uranyl oxalate to settle. The oxalate is then thoroughly washed, filtered, and dried in a vacuum desiccator and then in air at 110°C for 3 hours. The oxalate has the formula $UO_2(C_2O_4) \cdot 3H_2O$. This, together with recrystallized oxalic acid, is used to make the above solution. If very pure uranyl sulfate is available, uranyl sulfate may be used instead of uranyl oxalate. The solution used to titrate the oxalic acid is 0.1 N $KMnO_4$. The other reagent required is 96 per cent sulfuric acid.

Light Source. The lamp used is a G.E. 275-watt sun lamp. The approximate spectral distribution is given in Table E-II.

TABLE E-II

APPROXIMATE SPECTRAL DISTRIBUTION OF
G.E. 275-WATT SUN LAMP

Wavelength, Å	Relative Intensity
3967	0.041
3020	0.117
3130	0.353
3350	0.086
3650	1
4050	0.288
4350	0.468
5460	0.290
5790	0.072

Procedure. Clamp a 50-cc beaker to a ring stand, with the beaker resting on the base. Place a Pyrex plate or a Pyrex watch glass over the beaker. Clamp a crystallizing dish, approximately 10 cm in diameter, to the ring stand so as to be centered directly above the beaker, with the bottom of the dish about 1 cm from the top of the beaker. Fill the crystallizing dish with water to about $\frac{1}{2}$ cm from the top of the dish. (Use distilled water if available.) Clamp the sun lamp in a position directly centered over the crystallizing dish, with the light pointing downward into the crystallizing dish. The glass surface of the lamp should be positioned about $1\frac{1}{2}$ cm above the top of the crystallizing dish. Wrap aluminum foil about the setup to prevent exposure to long radiation. (CAUTION: Do not look directly at the lamp; if possible, wear eyeglasses or goggles during the exposure.)

Pipette 10 cc of the acinometer solution into the beaker. Place a sheet of black paper over the beaker. Turn on the lamp. After making sure the lamp has reached its full intensity (bluish light), which takes about 1 minute, remove the black paper and note the time. After 30 minutes turn off the lamp and remove the beaker containing the solution. Pipette 5 cc of the solution and empty it into a 50-cc Erlenmeyer flask. Add 1 cc of concentrated sulfuric acid carefully. (Heat will develop during this operation.) Fill a 10-cc burette with the 0.1 N KMnO$_4$ to the zero mark. Place the Erlenmeyer flask containing the solution on a hot plate and heat to approximately 60-70°C. Titrate with the KMnO$_4$ solution, adding the solution slowly dropwise and swirling the Erlenmeyer flask. When one drop imparts a permanent purple color, the end point is reached. Read the burette. Refill the burette. Pipette 5 cc of unexposed actinometer solution and empty it into a 50-cc Erlenmeyer flask. Titrate as above. (CAUTION: Do not expose the stock solution to excessive light.) If time permits, repeat the above experiment, using an exposure of 15 minutes.

CALCULATION OF PHOTONS ABSORBED

Calculate the difference in the number of cubic centimeters of KMnO$_4$ used in the two titrations. Multiply this by the normality of KMnO$_4$. This gives the number of milli-equivalents of oxalic acid destroyed by the light. Divide this by 2 to obtain the number of millimoles of oxalic acid destroyed. Multiply this by Avogadro's number (6.02×10^{23} atoms per mole) and divide by 1000 to get the number of molecules of oxalic acid destroyed. Divide this by the quantum yield Φ listed in Table E-1. (Use 0.5 for the 3650-Å line, as this is the most intense line in the light source used.) This gives the number of photons absorbed by the solution. In more accurate work, light of a particular wavelength would be used, using a monochromator or filters to isolate the given wavelength. Also, for more accurate work the solution should be stirred during exposure and kept at a constant temperature.

PLANT IRRADIATION EFFECTS

Sunflower seeds were X-irradiated at various doses and planted along with unirradiated control seed. Lots as follows are included: 0 and 500 r, and 1, 2, 5, 10, 20, 30, and 50 kr.

This demonstration illustrates little or no noticeable effects at the lower doses, leaf mottling and leaf distortions at intermediate doses, and severe distortion and stunting at the higher doses.

Dry seeds are much more radioresistant than growing plants. If a seedling plant had been irradiated, much greater damage would have taken place. For example, 2000 r or above is sufficient to kill a young sunflower seedling.

In addition to these visible radiation symptoms, ionizing radiation also produces genetic effects and this procedure has been used by geneticists and plant breeders to produce variation in breeding stock.

Packets of seed, unirradiated and irradiated at various doses, have been prepared for distribution among the students for use in later classroom demonstrations. The seed may be planted in soil, supplied with moisture, and should be maintained under conditions favorable for plant growth (temperature between 70-80°F and sufficient light).

UPTAKE AND DISTRIBUTION OF P^{32} IN TOMATO PLANT

Place a 6-inch test tube, about half-filled with water, in a 600-ml beaker partially filled with sand. Transfer about 2 to 3 μc P^{32} as $KH_2P^{32}O_4$ in solution form into the test tube. Cut the stem of a tomato plant near the base, remove one or two of the lowermost leaves, and make a new cut just above the severed end of the stem while the stem is under water, and place the stem end of the plant into the test tube. Uptake of radiophosphorus may be observed by monitoring various parts of the plant at intervals with a portable end-window counter. After about $\frac{1}{2}$ to 1 hour, leaves may be removed and placed on no-screen X-ray film; the film may be developed the following day and positive prints may be made for members of the class.

Rubber gloves should be worn by personnel handling P^{32} as well as active plant material.

THE RESPONSE OF YEAST CELLS TO IRRADIATION

The rate at which organisms in a given population are killed with increasing amounts of irradiation is called the dose response. If the per cent of deaths is plotted against the dose delivered to the population, using ordinary graph paper, an S-shaped curve is usually found, sloping gently upwards initially, then steeply, and finally leveling off as it approaches 100 per cent. For the sake of reference, as the most reproducible point on the curve, workers usually use the term LD_{50}, the lethal dose required to kill half of the population. The LD_{50} varies greatly from species to species. It is the purpose of this experiment to demonstrate the dose response of a population of yeast cells to irradiation, in this case, ultraviolet light.

MATERIALS

Dry yeast
Sterile glass or plastic Petri dishes
Sterile pipettes graduated in 0.1-ml divisions
Sterile DIFCO Potato Dextrose Agar
GE Germicidal lamp

METHOD

Weigh out 1 gm of dry yeast.
Suspend in 1 liter H_2O and mix very well.
Transfer 1 ml to 999 ml of H_2O and mix thoroughly. (Further dilution may be necessary, depending on the sample of yeast.)
Pipette 3 ml of the final dilution of the yeast cells into a Petri dish.
Irradiate with ultraviolet light for various lengths of time.
Spread samples of 0.1 ml of irradiated cells on potato dextrose agar in Petri dishes.
In the same manner "plate" samples of nonirradiated cells.

RESULTS

After 48 hours each surviving cell will have multiplied so that the daughter cells will form a visible colony.
Count the number of colonies formed from irradiated cells as well as untreated control samples.
Plot per cent survivors against time of exposure to ultraviolet light.
Compute LD_{50}.

EFFECTS OF RADIATION OF MAMMALS

DEMONSTRATION

The rats shown in the demonstration received 700 roentgens four days ago. The following observations can usually be made.

External. The irradiated rat is listless, sickly looking; the fur may be ruffled and unkempt; diarrhea may be evident; and he has lost 15-20 per cent of his body weight.

Internal. The *stomach* is distended. The *small intestine* shows multiple small hemorrhages, the *intestinal mucosa* has sloughed off and the *spleen* is greatly reduced in size, usually pale in color. The *thymus* has almost disappeared. The *adrenals* may still be enlarged.

Microscopic. The *red blood cells* and *white blood cells* are decreased in number. There is almost complete cessation of cell division in the *bone marrow, spleen* and *small intestine* as well as the *testes* or *ovaries*.

LIQUID-LIQUID EXTRACTION SEPARATION

SUPPLIES

Three 60-ml cylindrical separatory funnels
Ring stand, 3 clamps, and holders
Graduated measuring tube
Small beakers

Feed. 0.75 gm dl [Co en$_2$C$_2$O$_4$] Cl (red), 0.28 gm dl [Co en$_3$] Cl$_3$ (yellow), 16.0 g sodium salicylate, dissolved in water and diluted 100 ml. (The en refers to ethylene diamine, H$_2$NCH$_2$CH$_2$NH$_2$; the C$_2$O$_4$ is the oxalate radical.)

Solvent. 50 ml of tributyl phosphate, i.e., $(n\text{-}C_4H_9O)_3PO$, diluted to 100 ml with *n*-heptane (or with benzene or toluene).

Scrub. 16.0 gm of sodium salicylate dissolved in water and diluted to 100 ml.

OPERATION

Into each of the separatory funnels, numbered successively 1, 2, and 3, is introduced 20 ml of SOLVENT. Then a 20-ml portion of FEED is introduced into separatory funnel No. 1. The two phases are mixed by shaking for one minute. After phase disengagement, the lower (aqueous) phase is transferred to separatory funnel No. 2. A 20-ml portion of SCRUB is now added to No. 1. Both No. 1 and No. 2 are now shaken.

After phase disengagement, the lower phase of No. 2 is transferred to No. 3; then the lower phase of No. 1 is transferred to No. 2. A 20-ml portion of SCRUB is now added to No. 1. All three contactors are now shaken.

After phase disengagement, it may be seen from the colors of the various samples that No. 1 contactor contains pure $[Co\ en_3]^{+3}$ in the upper phase, and that No. 3 contains pure $[Co\ en_2\ C_2O_4]^{+1}$ in the lower phase, thus demonstrating a solvent separation of these two ions.

CONCLUSION

In line with the normal generalization it is found that, other factors canceling, the higher the valence state of a cation (or in this case positive charge), the greater its tendency to extract as part of an ion-pair entity into an organic extractant from an aqueous phase.

COPRECIPITATION EXPERIMENT

Put about 1000 c/m of tracer iodide in 2 ml of water, and add two drops of 0.1 M silver nitrate. With a sufficiently activated tracer, the iodide concentration should be too low to give a precipitate. If not, dilute with distilled water.

Put an identical portion of iodide into 2 ml of water, add 2 drops of 0.1 M sodium chloride solution, and stir. To this solution add 2 drops of the silver nitrate and 1 drop saturated ammonium nitrate; stir, heat to coagulate on a water bath, and centrifuge. Mount 0.5 ml of the supernatant liquid on a counting plate, dry and count. Decant the remaining supernatant from the silver chloride, add 1-2 ml of water, stir, centrifuge, and decant. Slurry the solid onto a counting plate with a small portion of water, dry, and count. Interpret results.

The experiment may be extended by having variable excesses of chloride in the solution over the amount of silver added to form the precipitate, and seeing how the carrying of iodide is affected by various degrees of incomplete precipitation of the chloride.

ION EXCHANGE SEPARATION

SUPPLIES

1. *Glass column:* 6 mm ID, 20 cm length, drawn to drip tip at bottom, fire polished at top to receive flexible tubing.

2. Small plug of *glass wool* pushed, by a wire, into small tip of column to serve as support for resin bed.

3. *Resin:* A sulfonic cation exchange resin, Dowex 50 X 8 W, passes 400 mesh. (The X 8 represents 8 per cent cross-linked; the W indicates white form of resin as opposed to the normal off-brown, unbleached, less expensive form, which has essentially the same characteristics except that "color separations" are difficult to observe in the column.)

4. *Auxiliary equipment:* ring stand, support clamps, support ring, globe separatory funnel for eluting agent, flexible tubing, transfer pipette, small measuring pipette or container, pipette control, small beakers.

5. *Feed:* 1.50 gm dl [Co en$_2$ C$_2$O$_4$] Cl (red), 0.57 gm dl [Co en$_3$] Cl$_3$ (yellow) dissolved in water and diluted to 100 ml, i.e., 0.05 meq of each complex per ml.

6. *Eluting agent:* 11.7 gm NaCl dissolved in water and diluted to 100 ml, i.e., 2 M NaCl.

FORMATION OF RESIN BED

The column is clamped in position with the top connected by a 50-cm length of flexible tubing to the separatory funnel held in the ring. (The tube should be reasonably taut.)

The system is now filled with water and *all air bubbles* removed by tapping the column or tubing with the finger. If necessary, the flow may be interrupted by placing the finger over the effluent tip. The water is then allowed to flow out until only a few milliliters remain in the separatory funnel. A slurry of the resin (about 3.0 gm of resin in 50 ml of water) is now added to the separatory funnel and the water allowed to flow slowly from the system until a mat of resin has built up on the glass wool plug. (The first water issuing from the tip may be cloudy with suspended resin.) Note that the 3.0 gm of resin refers to the resin "as received," which is approximately 50 per cent water by weight. *Do not dry the resin.*

Approximately an hour is required for the bed to settle properly.

After the resin bed has settled, the tubing is disconnected from the top. The water is removed from the top of the bed by means of a transfer pipette, leaving perhaps a 1-mm depth of water, *just before introducing the feed.*

(It is *imperative* that the liquid level never fall below the top of the resin bed, since bubbles of air will become entrapped in the bed in such a case.)

INTRODUCTION OF FEED AND ELUTING AGENT

A 0.5-ml portion of FEED is introduced by means of a transfer pipette. (The tip of the pipette should be at the surface of the water on the bed, and the liquid should be added slowly so that the top of the resin bed is not disturbed.)

When the liquid level is again nearly at the surface of the resin bed, a 0.5-ml sample of water is added.

When the liquid level is again nearly at the surface of the resin bed, the column is filled to the top with ELUTING AGENT and this level is maintained until attachment of the ELUTING AGENT reservoir as follows.

The same tubing-and-funnel assembly previously used in preparing the resin bed is now thoroughly rinsed, then partially filled with ELUTING AGENT. The liquid is allowed to flow into a clean beaker until the tubing is filled. At this point the stopcock is closed and the ELUTING AGENT in the beaker returned to the separatory funnel. The tubing (full of liquid) is now attached to the top of the column.

The stopcock is now opened and *all air bubbles removed* by tapping. The height of the separatory funnel is now adjusted so that the liquid level in the funnel is approximately 20 cm above the top of the resin bed.

The *elution rate* may now be controlled by varying the height of the separatory funnel.

CONCLUSIONS

It will be found that the feed is absorbed onto the resin bed in a narrow band which appears red (the yellow being effectively masked). As elution proceeds, this band is seen to split into a narrow yellow band above and a broad red band below. After further elution, a region of clear resin appears above the yellow band and a region of clear resin appears between the yellow band and the red band. With further elution, the red band continues to move down the column and continues to widen. Ultimately, a red liquid effluent appears from the column.

These results demonstrate that the $[Co\ en_3]^{+3}$ is held by the exchanger more tenaciously than is the $[Co\ en_2\ C_2O_4]^{+1}$ and that the separation of these ions by ion exchange is feasible.

In general, other factors canceling, the higher the valence state (or in this case positive charge) of a cation, the greater its tendency to be absorbed by a cation exchange resin.

DETERMINATION OF SOLUBILITY PRODUCT OF SILVER IODIDE USING IODINE TRACER

From the equilibrium concept, it is known that for difficultly soluble salts the product of ion concentrations, at saturation, is a constant K at a given temperature. With silver iodide, for example,

$$K = (Ag^+)(I^-).$$

With materials as insoluble as silver iodide, determination of the value of the solubility product, K, is difficult. The experiment to be described makes use of a radioactive tracer method for measuring the low concentration of iodide in the presence of excess silver ion.

SOLUTIONS

(1) Silver nitrate solution, accurately made up, c. 0.1 mole/liter.
(2) Potassium iodide solution, ca. 0.1 mole/liter.
(3) Trace radioactive iodide.

Counting plates, heat lamp, centrifuge tubes, ammonium nitrate solution (saturated).

PROCEDURE

Add radioactive tracer to a volume of the KI solution sufficient for the experiments, so that each milliliter contains several thousand counts per minute of active iodide.   To a series of accurately measured 1.0-ml aliquots of the KI solution in 15-ml centrifuge tubes add, respectively, accurately measured 0.2-, 0.4-, 0.6-, 0.8-ml portions of the silver nitrate, stir, make up to 2.0 ml, and heat in the water bath.   Centrifuge; if there seems to be colloidal solid in the supernate of the tubes, heat and centrifuge again.   Take a 0.2-ml aliquot of each supernatant, mount on a counting plate, dry under the heat lamp (avoiding decomposition), and count.   Calculate the total activity in the supernatant liquid, and plot activity against volume of silver nitrate.   Extrapolation of the linear relation to zero activity gives a standardization of the iodide solution, relative to the accurately known silver nitrate concentration.

For the actual determination of dissociation use the same KI but with 50,000 to 100,000 c/m of activity per milliliter.   Take a small accurate aliquot of the solution to determine the precise ratio of activity to iodide concentration.   Add, to identical accurate 1.0-ml portions of the KI in centrifuge tubes, 0.2-, 0.4-, 9.6-, and 0.8-ml, accurately measured, *excesses* of silver nitrate solution over the equivalent volume determined in the first part of the experiment.   Make up to 3.0 ml.   Heat in the water bath to coagulate the solid, and centrifuge.   Mount 0.5-ml accurate aliquots on counting plates, dry, and count.   Calculate the final concentration of iodide from the activity fraction; calculate the final concentration of silver ion, and the solubility product, in each of the determinations.

NOTE: If the AgI coagulation gives trouble, add a drop or two of saturated ammonium nitrate solution.

EXPERIMENT ON ISOTOPIC EXCHANGE

With the availability of tracers it has become possible to follow the paths of certain atoms in the presence of other atoms of the same chemical species.   It is therefore possible to follow what happens when two chemical forms of the same element are mixed even when there is no net chemical reaction, and to show whether there is interchange of atoms between these chemical forms.

A particularly nice form of isotopic exchange, for pedagogical purposes, is one which demonstrates the mobile nature of chemical equilibrium at the same time. The exchange involves the equilibrium in the formation of a complex ion, viz.,

$$I^- + I_2 = I_3^- \ [= (I - I - I)^-].$$

If one starts with the tracer (e.g., radioactive I^{131} as the iodide) and inactive iodine, separation of the iodine (e.g., by solvent extraction) shows the buildup of activity in the I_2 which was originally inactive. This demonstrates not only the exchange of iodine atoms between the iodide and iodine, but that in maintaining the equilibrium in the equation above, the complex ion is continually dissociating and being reformed, according to the statistical demands of the equilibrium:

$$K = (I^-)(I_2)/(I_3^-) = 1.4 \times 10^{-3}.$$

EXPERIMENTAL

Solutions

(1) Aqueous KI solution, concentration accurately known, ca. 0.1 mole/liter. If yellow, must be decolorized before use with dilute reducing agent, e.g., bisulfite or thiosulfate.

(2) Iodine in carbon tetrachloride solution, concentration known, ca. 0.1 mole/liter.

(3) $NaHSO_3$ solution; saturated ammonium nitrate.

(4) Active trace iodide.

Experiment. Add active iodide to the KI solution in such volume that each milliliter contains about 1×10^5 counts per minute at the experimental geometry. Put 2.0 ml of this iodide in a small separatory funnel, add 2.0 ml of the carbon tetrachloride solution of iodine, and shake vigorously for 2-3 minutes (accurately timed). Let the phases separate, separate the carbon tetrachloride solution (bottom layer) from the aqueous, add 1 ml of pure carbon tetrachloride solvent to the funnel, and drain it out, without shaking, adding to the iodine-laden solvent. Make these combined organic layers to 5.0 ml in a volumetric flask.

Take a 1.0-ml aliquot of the organic solution, decolorize carefully with a minimum amount of aqueous sodium bisulfite solution, and add a small excess of silver nitrate to precipitate the iodide. Addition of a drop or two of ammonium nitrate will hasten coagulation of colloid. Centrifuge down the silver iodide, and test completeness of precipitation by adding another drop of silver nitrate to the supernatant. Decant clear supernatant, draining as completely as possible, then slurry the AgI precipitate with a small volume of distilled water and transfer to a counting plate. Dry preparation under a heat lamp, being careful not to heat so hot that the silver salt decomposes. Count in a G-M counter. Compare this count with that obtained by taking aliquot of the *original* active KI solution used in the equilibration, precipitating with $AgNO_3$, and mounting on a similar plate. Make all counts to be compared at about the same time. (Why?)

Using the *same* portion of aqueous KI as in the first equilibration, add a fresh portion of iodine-bearing carbon tetrachloride, equilibrate for as closely as possible the same length of time with the same shaking, and repeat the preparation of a counting sample. Count. Compare the two results.

Calculate the efficiency of equilibration in the two experiments, assuming that the atom exchange process itself is instantaneous. Compare the efficiencies for the two experiments.

CAUTION: Do not breathe the iodine fumes after equilibration.

METALLURGY EXPERIMENTS*

The metallurgy laboratory experiments are designed to give the participants an opportunity to make a fuel element of the type that is used in the Materials Testing Reactor at Arco, Idaho. This fuel element is composed of a core of uranium-aluminum alloy which is completely covered with a cladding of commercially pure aluminum. The core alloy contains the fissionable material which is contained within the aluminum cladding, whose purposes are to prevent the water in the reactor from corroding away the fissionable material and to contain the fission products that are formed as a result of the fission process in the reactor.

SAFETY PRECAUTIONS

1. There is no radiation problem in the laboratory, because none of the uranium has been irradiated. Smoking is permitted, but no food or drink should be taken in the laboratory.

2. The Fabrication Laboratory is considered to be slightly contaminated owing to the possibility that uranium oxide dust may be distributed. However, we have had the room surveyed and there is not any detectable contamination on floors and benches. The fluid in the cutoff wheel is slightly contaminated.

3. Everyone is to wear a white lab coat to keep street clothes clean.

4. Wear a face shield when within 10 feet of molten metal whether working with it or just looking at it. Take no chances with your eyesight.

5. Wear heavy asbestos gloves when handling thermally hot materials from the furnace and at the rolling mill.

6. Wash hands occasionally when at polishing benches in order to remove any possible contamination due to the coolant.

7. Since there has been too little time for proper instruction in their use, please DO NOT OPERATE the following equipment:

    a. 30-kw Motor Generator Set

    b. Rolling Mill

    c. Universal Testing Machine.

METHOD OF CONDUCTING EXPERIMENTS

The experimental equipment and supplies have been prepared in advance. The students are to be divided into 3 groups of about 7 each. An instructor will work

*Prepared by J.E. Baird and R.F. Friddle of the International Institute of Nuclear Science and Engineering, Argonne National Laboratory.

with each group as a leader and the students will be helpers. The students will do almost all of the experimental work under the careful guidance of the instructor.

The following experiments aim at a real understanding of the problem of making fuel elements for reactors, as well as at an insight into the principles of metallurgy.

EXPERIMENT 1: MAKE URANIUM-ALUMINUM ALLOY BY MELTING THE ELEMENTS IN A HIGH-FREQUENCY INDUCTION FURNACE

The materials to be melted are aluminum wire and uranium. The alloy to be made is 90 per cent aluminum and 10 per cent uranium. The charge will consist of 500 gm of aluminum wire and about 60 gm of uranium metal. The apparatus for melting includes the following items:

The mold. The rectangular graphite mold is made in two sections: the casting cavity is $\frac{3}{4}$ in. thick by $2\frac{1}{2}$ in. wide by 6 in. deep. The mold is bolted together.

Melting crucible. This is made of graphite, $2\frac{3}{4}$ in. ID by $3\frac{3}{4}$ in. OD by $4\frac{1}{2}$ in. high. It has a $\frac{1}{4}$-in.-diameter hole in the bottom.

Stopper rod. This is of $\frac{3}{4}$-in. diameter with a machined tip to fit in the pouring hole at the bottom of the crucible. This keeps the molten metal in the crucible until the molten fuel is ready to pour.

The insulation. The large magnesia crucible is $5\frac{1}{2}$ in. ID by $6\frac{1}{2}$ in. OD by $12\frac{3}{4}$ in. high. The space between the insulating crucible and the graphite melting crucible is to be filled with zirconia bubbles.

This equipment is to be assembled in the following manner. The mold is bolted together and placed inside the large magnesia crucible. A piece of asbestos paper, $5\frac{1}{2}$ in. in diameter with a $\frac{3}{4}$-in. hole in the center, is placed on top of the graphite mold. Then a small zirconia brick, $\frac{1}{2}$ in. thick with a hole that lines up with the pouring hole in the crucible, is placed on top of the asbestos paper. The crucible is placed on top of the brick. The purpose of the brick is to keep the crucible hot and the mold cold during the melting operation. Zirconia bubbles are then poured around the graphite crucible to provide insulation for the side walls. Dry lime is sprinkled in the bottom of the melting crucible to keep the metal from sticking to the graphite. The stopper rod is put in place and the aluminum wire slipped down over the stopper rod. Since this melt is to be made in air, the assembly is placed within the high-frequency induction coil. This is a four-turn coil, 7 in. ID by 6 in. high. The coil is water cooled. The current frequency from the motor generator set is 10,000 cycles per second. The graphite crucible will be heated red hot by induction from the 10,000 reversals per second of the current in the induction coil.

MAKING THE MELT

During the melting operation everyone will wear a face shield and asbestos gloves. Shortly after the power is turned on for the induction coil, the graphite crucible will become red hot. In a few minutes the aluminum wire will melt down. It is necessary to hold the stopper rod in place with a graphite rod to prevent it from floating in the molten aluminum. Skim the dross from the surface of the molten aluminum with a graphite rod. The uranium is then dropped into the molten aluminum. After a few minutes stir the melt vigorously with a graphite rod to be sure that it is homogeneous; this is like stirring coffee to dissolve the sugar. Then skim the melt to remove the dross from the top.

Take the temperatures of the molten metal with an optical pyrometer. This is an instrument which is used in taking temperatures in a steel mill and is based on matching the color of a heated filament in the optical pyrometer with the color of the melt. Temperatures will range from 850° to 1000°C. The instructor will cut down on the power going into the induction coil so the melt will cool down to 800°C. At this temperature the ingot is cast by lifting up the stopper rod, thus permitting the molten metal to run out of the hole in the bottom of the crucible and down into the mold. The metal solidifies in the mold in a few seconds. The power to the induction coil is shut off. The crucible cools to a black heat in a few minutes, and then the entire assembly is removed from the induction coil and emptied into a large tray. Everything is hot and everyone should be wearing heavy asbestos gloves.

Remove the ingot from the split graphite mold. Cool it in water. Take the ingot to the abrasive cutoff wheel where sections will be cut from top and bottom for samples.

EXPERIMENT 2: HOT-ROLLING THE URANIUM-ALUMINUM ALLOY

The ingot, from which the top and bottom have been cut, is approximately $\frac{3}{4}$ in. thick by $2\frac{1}{2}$ in. wide by 4 in. long. It is placed in a muffle furnace and heated to 550°C. Since there is so much more aluminum than uranium in the ingot, it looks very much like an ordinary aluminum alloy and can be heated in the air without any danger of contamination of the air. Allow the ingot to soak in the furnace for about half an hour. Put on heavy asbestos gloves to remove the hot ingot from the furnace for rolling. Take care that no one puts hands into the rolls on the rolling mill. The ingot must be pushed into the rolls with a wooden stick. An instructor will be at the mill to start and stop it. Roll the ingot in the rolling mill, one person feeding it into the flat rolls on one side and another person catching it on the opposite side of the rolls and passing it back to the first person. About 0.030 in. is reduced in each pass.

After several passes, place the ingot back in the furnace for reheating. The ingot is finally rolled to a slab $\frac{1}{4}$ in. thick and a foot long. The rolled slab can be cooled in water.

EXPERIMENT 3: CAST CLADDING

Cut a piece, about $2\frac{1}{4}$ in. by $1\frac{7}{8}$ in., from the $\frac{1}{4}$-in. rolled slab. Mark the slab with a stylus. It will be cut in the abrasive cutoff wheel, which has a Plexiglas shield to keep the cutting fluid from splashing on the people operating it.

This piece of 10% *uranium*-90% *aluminum alloy is the fuel for one fuel plate.* It is to be thoroughly dried and placed in a special cladding mold. The cladding mold contains five locating pins, four on one side and one on the other, which keep the piece of uranium-aluminum alloy suspended in the middle of the mold with $\frac{1}{4}$ in. of space all around it.

Everyone is to wear asbestos gloves and face shield. Scoop a ladle of molten aluminum from the special melting pot, skim the dross from the surface, and pour the molten aluminum into the cladding mold so that it completely covers the uranium-aluminum alloy. The molten aluminum freezes quickly. Then take apart the cladding mold and remove the clad uranium-aluminum alloy. In this "sandwich" the uranium-aluminum alloy is the meat and the aluminum cladding is the bread. The cladding, of course, contains the five small holes from the centering pins in the cladding mold. Heat the sandwich in the muffle furnace at 550°C for 15 minutes. Then remove it from the furnace, place it between two hot plates of stainless steel, and put it in the compression head of the Universal Testing Machine. Here it is pressed hot to approximately $\frac{5}{8}$-in. thickness to close the holes left by the centering pins and also to help bond the uranium-aluminum alloy core to the aluminum cladding. After this hot pressing, place the sandwich back in the furnace at 550°C to heat for rolling.

EXPERIMENT 4: ROLLING THE FUEL PLATE

Remove the sandwich from the furnace after 15 minutes and roll it in successive steps of about 0.025 in. per pass until it is about 0.050 in. thick. Wear asbestos gloves for the hot-rolling operation. Take turns in feeding and in receiving on the rolling mill. It will be necessary to reheat about 4 times during the rolling operation. The length of most of the fuel elements will be about 2 feet. It looks like an ordinary piece of aluminum sheet.

EXPERIMENT 5: INSPECTION OF THE FUEL ELEMENT

Cut sections from the fuel element on the abrasive cutoff wheel. Polish the cross-sectional surface at the polishing benches, using a 240 grit paper on the polishing wheel. Then etch the piece of fuel element in hot concentrated sodium hydroxide solution. This solution darkens only the uranium-aluminum alloy, while the aluminum cladding remains bright. Looking at the cross section of fuel plate, you will see the center of the fuel plate to be uranium-aluminum alloy which is completely surrounded by aluminum. This is visible to the naked eye. Place the etched piece under the microscope and examine it at magnifications up to 50×.

SAMPLES FOR TEACHING AIDS

The samples listed below were made available for instructional purposes to teachers who performed the foregoing experiment.

1. A sample of a uranium bar, 0.4 in. in diameter by 0.7 in. long, embedded in clear Lucite. This is to be used for density determination of uranium. Students will have to know the density of the Lucite.
2. A piece of the 10% uranium-90% aluminum alloy ingot made in Experiment 5.
3. A piece of the cross section of the fuel plate, 1 in. by 3 in., that had been etched in sodium hydroxide to show the core and the clad.

INDEX